ABORTION: The Trojan Horse

A human look at a new dilemma

ABORTION:
The Trojan Horse

**Janet M. Patterson and
R. C. Patterson, Jr., M.D.**

THOMAS NELSON INC.
NASHVILLE / NEW YORK

Published by Thomas Nelson, Inc. in Nashville, Tennessee.
Manufactured in the United States of America

Library of Congress Cataloging in Publication Data

Patterson, Janet.
  Abortion: the Trojan horse.

    1. Abortion—United States. 2. Abortion—Psycho-
logical aspects. 3. Parent and child. I. Patterson,
Robert C., 1912-   joint author. II. Title.
[DNLM: 1. Abortion, Induced. HQ767 P317a]
HQ767.5.U5P38   301   74-14637
ISBN 0-8407-5583-X

To My Patients

Contents

PART ONE: BACKGROUNDS 13
  1 Women 15
  2 The Law 23
  3 The Abortion 35

PART TWO: PROBLEMS 47
  4 Communication 49
  5 To Marry or Not to Marry 65
  6 These are the 70s 71
  7 Suicide 83
  8 Our Children 95
  9 Mother Can Have an Abortion, Too 109
 10 Sex, Education, Revolution, and War 113

PART THREE: MORALS 121
 11 Is Abortion Murder? 123
 12 Jesus People 133
 13 Ethics 143

PART FOUR: A SOLUTION 155
 14 Options to Abortion 157

PART FIVE: MEDICAL 167
 15 First Intercourse 169
 16 Doctors' Attitudes 173

vii

Preface

Jane and her mother were sitting in my office crying. Jane was sixteen, not very attractive, but *more than slightly* pregnant. She was unmarried. She wanted an abortion.

What could I tell her?

I am a gynecologist. My own personal attitude toward abortion has developed out of my professional practice independent of moral and religious concerns—but heavily influenced by the appearance in my office day after day of young girls like Jane. Many of my colleagues have made the same pilgrimage I have. Because we are at the point where actual decisions are made, I think that we have something of value to say that has not been said. Hence this book.

Why do I call abortion a "Trojan Horse?"

In case your recollection of ancient history is fuzzy, let's recall a little of Homer's account. The Greeks had unsuccessfully besieged Troy. One night they decamped, leaving a giant wooden effigy of a horse on the plain before the walls of Troy. The Trojans, elated with victory, brought the "Horse" into the city. It was filled with soldiers who came out the next night to open the gates for the returning Greeks. Ever since, the "Trojan Horse" has been the symbol of the deceiving element within something that appears to be "Good."

I am convinced that the present legalization of abortion could well be the "Trojan Horse" of our generation. To many, liberalized abortion appears to liberate "Woman." But, does it? Like so many "solutions" of our time, this one is not as "good" as it seems. Why do we say this?

It's easy for doctors and scientists to answer the practical problems of such matters as birth control, methods of abortion, and alternatives to abortion. But the human problems are as difficult as the progress of civilization itself. Is abortion freedom or genocide? What's wrong with teenagers? Why is there a sexual revolution? Is marriage obsolete? Why doesn't my child talk to me? In these questions, the specifics of the medical field tangle with the subjective abstractions of human thought.

Every day the obstetrician and gynecologist is apt to have three or four mind-blowing questions tossed his way. Often a patient comes to the doctor for specific complaints, but frequently she is also asking his advice for the problems of human living. The doctor as well as the patient needs ground-thinking for a decision base. The former can't play God in a white coat; but, for his own peace of mind, he needs to think through problems presented because many women and girls are desperate. Both doctor and patient need to examine the issues and find a hitching post. Such is the purpose of this book. It is not a question of yes or no to the abortion as much as it is an effort to dissect the various issues and maybe, or maybe not, reach a conclusion. Solutions and viewpoints depend on variables. Certainly my conclusions or non-conclusions won't necessarily be yours, but they may help resolve your indecision and anxiety.

I am not a frustrated educator, minister, lawyer, or historian. I am a husband who loves Woman because I love my wife. I love children because I am a parent. As a doctor, I have heard more anguished cries from women in the past two years than ever before. Perhaps in this personal and oversimplified view of the issues in the "Trojan Horse" I can make cry-time a little shorter for them.

R. C. Patterson, Jr., m.d.

Part One: Backgrounds

What the person making a decision concerning abortion would be told by a good counselor regarding past events, certain background facts, and some basic presuppositions.

Jane Doe v. State of Georgia

In Jane Doe v. State of Georgia on January 22, 1973, the United States Supreme Court handed down the well-publicized decision that legalized abortion. It was a milestone of social law—and a victory for liberal forces. The Court ruled that the state could not interfere with a woman's right to decide with her physician to have an abortion within the first three months of pregnancy. During the second three months, the state could check the individual application for abortion, determine procedure, and prohibit the operation if the state deemed the grounds did not warrant the request. During the final weeks of pregnancy, the state would have the authority to prohibit abortion when there was no threat to the mother's life by carrying the baby to viability.

CHAPTER ONE

Women

Big, tough-looking Mr. Caldwell was eyeing me belligerently. "We don't want another baby, Doctor," he said firmly. "Our children are old enough to take care of themselves, and Mary is thirty-six. She's my bookkeeper since the children have grown up. Couldn't run the business without her. She wants an abortion."

I looked at Mrs. Caldwell, expecting confirmation, but Mrs. Caldwell wasn't confirming anything. "It's really your decision, Mrs. Caldwell," I prodded.

"We'll think about it, and I'll call you," she said.

Less than an hour later, Mrs. Caldwell called and left the message that she would not have an abortion. She wanted the baby. Apparently her husband just hadn't asked her first.

Women . . .

As a gynecologist, I was not particularly surprised at

Mrs. Caldwell. Male doctors do have some advantages in understanding the female. More so than most men, as the following quotation from a certain well-known French historical personality proves:

> Nature intended women to be our slaves—they are our property; we are not theirs. They belong to us, just as a tree that bears fruit belongs to a gardener. What a mad idea to demand equality for women!—Women are nothing but machines for producing children.
>   —NAPOLEON BONAPARTE

This from France? And yet French women had the most celebrated bedrooms in the world! The paradox is big enough to unglue a modern girl's eyelashes. And what about Napoleon and his wife Josephine, the beautiful Creole from the West Indies? She didn't even give him an heir, but she was enough to make Elizabeth Taylor look like a country girl. Josephine was Napoleon's slave? In the weeks of his early military conquest, he heard gossip about his new bride which prompted him to write her volumes of hate-love letters. He was wordy, but she happily and passionately continued her own conquests and pleasures. However, never underestimate the power of a vocal man. He was in Italy at the time and later wrote, "When I see an empty throne, I feel the urge to sit down on it." Not a particularly brilliant quote, but when you think it over, it rounds out the picture a bit. Despite Josephine's extracurricular parties, time proved that she deeply loved Napoleon. She even begged to share the dull life of Elba with him.

But that's enough about Napoleon and his ridiculous definition of women.

Men are forever talking about women. Who knows where it will lead? Usually it leads to sex. Who cares? Certainly not women, as long as they can pull their status a little further along civilization's trail.

American women have come a long way, all the way from chattel to suffrage to legal abortion and full rights over their body. Will abortion be a fallout for the human race? Or will it help build a beautiful new society in which children are born of love to be loved?

Women, your baby can be by choice, free choice. You, and you alone, can make the decision—not your husband, boyfriend, parents, doctor, or government. It is your life style, your belief, and your background that will help you decide.

No one can underestimate the power of "Woman." She is mother of men, but she is more, much more. In spite of the fact that she has lived and still lives in a world that gives men most of the advantages for advancement and leadership, she has made great contributions to civilization. As she is the symbol of beauty, so she is also the statues of liberty and justice. "Woman" has been a dynamic figure in all the great progressions of mankind. I'm not just speaking of historical exceptions like Helen of Troy, Cleopatra, Queen Isabella, Catherine of Russia, and Queen Elizabeth, but rather of the mass of women.

Pioneer Women

While French women were living it up in the bedroom, where was American Woman? She was on the farm, thumbing her Bible, cooking her Thanksgiving turkeys, and rating only an occasional honorable mention. Male historians give Pocahontas the best headlines of the day—which doesn't say much, but does show a certain ethnic liberalism in regard to women.

During the Revolution, Betsy Ross stitched together the flag. It was a good one, and she was awarded the contract to make all of them; so she sewed nice flags until she died at the age of eighty-four. Daughter Clarissa kept right on with the flags. The West was as heroically settled by pioneer women as by men, but we mostly hear of the Davy Crocketts and Sam Houstons who slept around in several pads. Some writings and drawings of the time do show bleak yards with nameless Woman surrounded by numerous children of various ages clinging to her long skirts. She often had a shotgun in her hand, so we presume that she was protecting her brood from Indians, murderers, and wolves. She was there working, feeding, begetting, training, and often fighting. Annie Oakley was an exception. One could throw a playing card in the air, and with her twenty-two rifle, she could hit that card a half dozen times before it touched the ground. Think that one over, and see where it gets you. Nowhere, I guess, except to male historians. Nevertheless, it is with Woman in true but silent partnership of advancement that this country pushed on to new frontiers.

By the end of the eighteenth century, the women of this country appeared to be totally trapped by pregnancies, bad health, and trivialization. The pedestal ideal with bows and flowers was prevalent. The bows and flowers theme was doubtless imported from France by way of traveling husbands, but the pedestal notion was American male to the core. They were virile enough, God knows, but they were also more than slightly moralistic in regard to their wives. The upper-class woman was protected from outside influences like education, exercise, and other more suggestive and provocative pursuits. This theme often extended into her own home social life. After a company dinner, she usually left the room with a swishing of her hoops, and the men settled into their brandy and conversations. She was protected and also dull and uninteresting. Hers was a cloistered and barricaded world, and she grew ill from babies, no exercise, and no interests. She was often seen at health spas, drinking mineral water and reclining on cots, suffering everything from general malaise to the traumas of children and tuberculosis. It wasn't such a good life.

The Fight Begins

American women officially bowed on the public stage by way of the antislavery movement. Lucretia Mott (1793–1880) was an early and sturdy abolitionist. She was sturdy in every sense of the word, and was elected to the World's Anti-Slavery Convention. She was not allowed to be seated because she was a woman. She, with several dozen other ladies, including Elizabeth Cady Stanton, had traveled three thousand miles for these historical sessions. This bit of male snobbery led to the beginning of the woman's rights movement. These rejected persons reacted logically, creatively, and intelligently to the situation. They were among the first educated women in the country, and it showed. Education always seems to be one of the first troublemakers from the underprivileged; no wonder men fought it for so long.

Ms. Mott and her associates felt that the plight of

women as human beings paralleled the plight of slaves. They reasoned that women were entitled to human rights also. They noticed the historical position of men, money, and power and concluded that man used his power to oppress blacks, classes, nations—and Woman.

The first rights' convention was held in 1848 in Seneca Falls, New York. The ladies were primarily concerned with educational advantages, equal property rights, and fair divorce laws.

At the time, Elizabeth Cady Stanton insisted that the right to vote should be included in the resolutions. Although the injection of the franchise was not popular with most of the other leaders of the convention, it was included. Ms. Stanton's father, a prominent New York judge, was so shocked by the radical idea of woman's suffrage that he came to Seneca Falls to see for himself whether or not his daughter was mentally rational. Men all over the country rose to magnificent resistance and argued that a woman's mind was not equal to a man's (possibly because of her "seasons and cycles"). The men argued and smirked a lot.

Suffrage became a big issue as women grew louder in demands for equal rights as citizens. In 1868, the Fourteenth Amendment gave voting rights to all males—and no women. In 1869, the National Woman Suffrage Association was founded, and fifty-one years later, women received voting status. It had been seventy-two years since the conception of the idea in the Seneca Falls Convention! In the meantime, women made appearances in great style all over the country by speaking and writing. It was "Show Time" everywhere. Women spoke passionately and dramatically on many subjects; sex, drinking, and temperance came out of the closet, too. People listened, but they often shouted disrupting, humiliating jeers and vituperatives. The press, that citadel of freedom, was especially vehement, violent, and vomitus. *And then came Woman in bloomers!!* She was the thunderbolt of the age. Civilization was surely doomed! Ah, well—poor man. How he suffers. That rib the Lord took from Adam hurt and continues to hurt.

In the meantime, Jane Adams had started one of the first social settlement houses in this country, and it had become an international model. Against great odds, Clara Barton founded the American Red Cross. Both were outstanding women, but theirs were not the only accomplishments. Many women picked up the humanitarian torch and helped move the efforts forward. All of this is to say that Woman has had to fight for every one of her rights from the mental to the physical. In the Biblical sense, she was born to be a helpmate of man in the monogamous context of love and under God. As "Man" became more and more "sex happy" and less and less "Godly," the status of Woman declined.

But the population steadily multiplied. Woman was doing her procreating job just fine.

Woman's Responsibilities

However, now women have the right of abortion. With this right is a choice that has more depth than any decision a single man will ever have the responsibility of making. A woman weighs the life or death of a human being when she chooses whether to abort or not to abort. Does she need time to ponder the momentous power now at her disposal? Will she act? We think she will, and with intuitive compassion and common sense. Consequently, the world will be a better place. There is always shock value in new freedom of any kind, momentous or trivial. There was a time when "ladies never smoked," and even now one hears dire words about the harm to the foetus from smoking. Women and biology are inseparable, but the fact is not insurmountable. Women will find the right answers.

Will the Birthrate Drop?

When abortion became legal, many expected the birthrate would plummet to new and alarming lows, and it did because America is admittedly over-prescribed to sex. However, adjustment in judgment and wisdom will be made. The trend will turn toward a less hasty and less emotionally expedient solution than abortion. This is not to say that abortion does not have its place. It is only to say that birth control is the better solution.

Since modern woman is as sexually desirable as Helen of Troy, man has blueprinted a law of abortion to help with her problems of sex. It is right that she should have the dignity of choice; the law promises help for many tragedies of women and children. Each woman knows that she must beware of the Greeks bearing gifts. The fact of abortion requires appraisal from women. Is she a woman first and mother second or vice versa? Each woman must make her own individual decision, not lightly, but ethically or prayerfully or both. Will the men please stop shouting and let the women decide!!

CHAPTER TWO

The Law

Mrs. Herndon was fifty years old and angry. She had come to the office on the pretense of having a check-up, but she really wanted to talk about her daughter-in-law who had recently had an abortion, much to Mrs. Herndon's disapproval. "Why shouldn't she have another baby?" she asked vehemently. "Four children aren't too many! I had six, and we made it. Not always easy, but not too hard either."

"Abortion is her legal choice," I began, bored because I have been asked the question so often.

"I hate abortion!" she interrupted, pounding her fist on the desk. "That law is evil—evil! Whatever is this country coming to? First they take prayer out of schools. And now, this! Doctor, why don't the doctors get together and do something?"

Mrs. Herndon's conclusion was a weak one. Doctors

don't get together to do much of anything. Once they are together, they don't agree on many subjects beyond the basics of medicine. I did not like to see the law raising Mrs. Herndon's blood pressure, but I hadn't had anything to do with changing the law, and there wasn't anything I really wanted to do about it. The law has been discussed so many times in my office that I have begun to feel that it is a person, ready and striking. Perhaps I should write a paper, Xerox it, and put dozens of copies in the reception room for all those people who want to bomb the Supreme Court. And what would I say if I did? I would say something like this:

The abortion law is a fact. Pro-con arguments don't have top billing anymore. We should be proud to live in a democracy where laws are changed to reflect customs and desires. This happened fast, yes, but it happened. If you are a conservative, you will continue to hit the doomsday bucket; but if you are a liberal, you will sail through the air. Although you may not have seen any need for change, millions did. If you live in suburbia or the provinces, you often miss the heartbeat of the city. Everybody knows that abortion involves moral and ethical explosions, and if you are impaled on the dilemma, then you are in good company. Doctors and ministers are, too. Fertile youth, as well as many of the more mature, often view the law joyfully.

You would be shocked if you knew how many are using abortion for birth control. But any way that you look at it, abortion is not a fun thing—mentally, morally, physically, or financially. If time proves that women abuse the law, then suitable amendments will be made. Meanwhile, educational and ethical health care agencies must organize to implement the humanitarian concept into a system that will speed the intent of the law and prohibit abuse.

How It Started

I wish you would stop asking how it all started. Look up Margaret Sanger in the encyclopedia. If she hadn't started it, somebody else would have. Anyway, she advocated birth control, though not abortion. But in the early nineteen hundreds, the idea of birth control had all of the impact of the atom bomb.

What do you suppose motivated Ms. Sanger? Her tubercular mother died at the age of forty-eight, having birthed eleven children. Not much of an epitaph, but it tells an old, old story, and it helped motivate Daughter Margaret.

Margaret Sanger was a nurse and worked for awhile in the slums of New York City. She was greatly burdened by the number of women and children who were hopelessly trapped by hunger, disease—and more children. She began to write pamphlets explaining birth control which she circulated among the poor. The old expression, "keep a woman pregnant and barefoot," expressed the sentiments of the time. It was this that Ms. Sanger was fighting. She was often arrested for her views, but she was Irish-stubborn. Gradually, people began to understand a little of what she was saying.

The exposure of slum problems and the publicizing of birth control offered help for sex-related problems in all classes of society. Men and women were completely naive and unsophisticated about birth control. Large families were prevalent, and the childbirth mortality rate of women was high. In the light of the present, the difficulties of Ms. Sanger's early crusade seem absurd, but at the time it was a big issue.

As citizens began to listen and help with Margaret Sanger's campaign, some states passed laws that allowed doctors to advise patients of birth control for the purpose of preventing disease. Furthermore, in some other states, laws against this information were less stringently enforced. Considering the lack of knowledge of contraception, it is natural that women should have secretly applauded and encouraged the male's double standard. Even the deepest sex pleasure and maternal love is strained under the baby-a-year system. Women are eternally practical; with a stethoscope on the past you can hear the average housewife saying: "Mr. Jones, why don't you take a cold bath?" Or better still, "Why don't you rush down to the saloon?" While this was not great birth control, it was certainly better than none. However, "Woman" could stall just so long; she was forever pregnant. She died frequently and early in childbirth, even when "Father" spent a lot of time at the saloon. So, sex was certainly no big deal for "Woman." If female sex relation is 98% mental and 2% physical, as I personally believe, fear of pregnancy must certainly have inundated the mental, which leaves you at 2%. Not much of a figure as statistics go.

Harsh laws against birth control and abortion had been passed during the Civil War to enforce morality, as well as a means to increase the population. Occasional medical abortions were gradually accepted when the life of the mother was in jeopardy. Doctors were invariably left with the birth control and abortion decision, but it was not until the 1930s that the American Medical Association officially acknowledged that birth control was legally a subject suitable for doctors to discuss professionally. The abortion course of action was still so grave that it was a matter of consultation with other doctors rather than the judgment of a single physician. This careful evaluation was due to the general attitudes against abortion, as well as to the high risks of infection from the procedure.

After World War II, antibiotics were in wide use and remarkably reduced incidences of infections. At the same time, births became less hazardous, and non-obstetrical complications which were medical (heart disease, diabetes, et cetera) could be handled with a great degree of safety. The result was fewer abortions.

Underworld Abortion Rings

Meanwhile women didn't wait for laws to change. They went to the underworld for abortions. The practices here were cruel, inhumane, barbaric, and costly. This was especially true in metropolitan areas where poverty and destitution were more rampant. Millions sought the abortion rings even though they knew that ruined health and death were the calculated risks.

A Do-It-Yourself Nightmare

Self-induced abortion attempts were a common occurrence. The side effects here were even more lethal! Wire coat hangers, knitting needles, slippery elm tree roots, vaginal introduction of detergents, and a number of other methods were used. The pain and suffering was incalculable, yet millions of women desperately chose this route. The battered child syndrome (with its story of delinquency and defeat through a long, long, dreary life) added to the picture of misery. In the light of modern medicine, the situation was a raw sore, but doctors and responsible citizens seemed to be looking the other way. The vast suffering of women and children appeared to be ignored.

The Call for Change

Although we cannot say that the public was truly unaware of the problem, there was not much impetus toward a solution even as late as 1965. Legalization of abortion as a solution seemed a well-kept secret, but a real power base was to be formed. In 1969, after vigorous activity by a comparative few, the National Association for Repeal of the Abortion Laws (NARAL) was officially founded with Lawrence Lader as chairman. He was a brilliant strategist and is to be credited with much of the success of the movement. Many prominent persons, including clergymen, doctors, and women liberators, as well as various organizations, joined in the political and public effort to force the issue to court.

Within a comparatively short period of time, about seventeen states liberalized their abortion laws, and four others reserved only token restrictions. Polls indicated that 53% of single women favored legalized abortion. Polls are often limited to single women because they are more easily and accurately shifted into reliable statistics than married women. Single women can be reached in centrally-located places like schools and offices, while married women are usually more available by phone or door-to-door contacts. In this latter case, levels of society, age, education, and affluence are important factors and make statistical conclusion more complex.

In states where abortion had become a legislative debate, threatening bitterness was erupting. Some groups opposing abortion carried placards lettered, "Murderers!" in red paint, while others displayed grotesque colored pictures of dead and mangled foetuses. The nature of the protest promised as much disruption as anti-war demonstrations.

Complicated Factors

The Supreme Court's decision on abortion came quickly because of an involved confluence of factors. The states, with their widely divergent local mores, were being pushed into different corners on abortion decisions. The issue was trapped between two emotional extremes; it could have become as destructive and chaotic as a hurricane. The nation's politicians, who are a breed with few heroes, showed little enthusiasm for battle, either for or against. The Catholic Church was a known block, but the other religious groups seemed to dance the two-step:

first one way and then the other. Was "pro or con foetus" also "pro or con Woman?" Was it "humanizing or de-humanizing?" Was it "genocide?" Or, was it "Population Control?" Dedicated and sincere people were on both sides of the question. Impassioned confrontations and protests seemed to promise little except emotional upheavals and compromises that would be unsatisfactory to all sides. It was rightly a question for the Supreme Court; we were headed for confusing havoc with widely variant rulings. The Court balanced the scales; liberalized abortion became law. The decision was not a vague, grey, "in between" one designed to please everyone but in reality pleasing no one. It was a strong decision.

Now, What Do We Have?

Freedom of choice makes the "abortion problem" a question of education, religion, and social welfare. It is a personal choice instead of a state decision.

Since our concern is no longer with debate, we need to take steps quickly to prevent abuse of the law. We are in a trial period. Professionals as well as volunteers need to roll up their sleeves and roll out their brains. If we do not want to remain in perpetual crisis, we must find adequate solutions for the new set of problems.

Sex Education

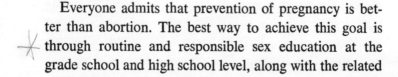
Everyone admits that prevention of pregnancy is better than abortion. The best way to achieve this goal is through routine and responsible sex education at the grade school and high school level, along with the related

subjects of parenthood and ethics. When such was first proposed, many religionists were quick to shout against such studies. I fear that they were still playing in a moral world of musical chairs and spin-the-bottle. They refused to look at reality and appeared to ignore the fact that moral chastity was often a fear-ridden concept instead of a moral choosing between right and wrong. Fear and ignorance are not Bible oriented tenets.

The individual is often too quick to pass blanket and mind-closing judgments on progressive thought. Issues need study. Just as prohibition drove drinking underground, the no-abortion law drove abortion in the same direction. In a police state, the law is admittedly more effective, but force is certainly not the answer. It only suppresses—and then only partially.

It is to be expected that the abortion rate will soar in the first few years because abortions will be used instead of birth control. However, if state and private educational systems meet the challenge, and if parents of the single girls will act maturely, we can build a better world with sane abortion statistics. Women will keep the home fires. They will not commit genocide. Experience will strengthen the moral fibers that have been weakened because those fibers are not only moral but also practical. Female motivations are as basic as nature itself. We must use telescopic vision on the future before we make dire predictions; we must accept the "now" of the times as the challenge that it is. We must accept the facts and use our brains to cope creatively. Negativism can only stand still or run backwards. It prevents us from realizing solutions that may be hiding in the back pocket.

Welfare and Abortion

In the area of welfare and abortion, it is assumed that this country will continue to follow somewhat the patterns set by New York. Office procedures for early abortion are necessarily used to offset the crowded situations of many hospitals. Agencies, working with professionals and volunteers, are already leading the way and offering help. Since doctors are too busy to care for the new and added burden of thousands of abortions, a staff of professionally trained interns and residents (they are M.D.'s) may be the answer. However the out-patient abortion bill has many chances for frightening abuse which could result in serious medical complications, immediate or delayed, as well as a life time of emotional and mental trauma. Adequate medical procedure and psychological counseling should be required. Such developments should be carefully screened by the government, as well as by the medical associations, on national and local levels.

Ideals Build Monsters

All of these necessary considerations bring very bad headaches. Ideals can build monsters within the Trojan Horse, and the old slogan "beware the Greeks bearing gifts" may have a modern version in the Supreme Court ruling. It will take many "think-tanks" to make the new abortion freedom feasible.

In addition to the above snares, many doctors are refusing to perform abortions for reasons of moral and medical judgment. This is certainly their incontestable prerogative.

The theory that has been launched as a humanitarian cause has many ugly seams which must be intelligently faced. A view of the past and present worldwide abortion information points up the inherent problems, but does not solve them. Heroics are necessary and, always, we are back to the obvious fact that birth control is the best answer. Great medical, scientific, educational, and welfare effort must be made. The popular terms "abortion on demand" and "social abortion" are frivolous slogans that belie the depth of the situation. The real issue has all the chaos of a parade, and makes one long wistfully for more peaceful issues. But this is a great nation. It has accepted, survived, and solved many crises, and it is not apt to drown in the moral revolution that it now faces on many fronts. We have the tools, the education, and the brains to accept the present as a creative challenge. Women power—and men power—will work together. To use an old expression, there is individual weakness, but there is common strength.

A Problem of Humanities

The record of other countries is of interest but of no great concern. We are indoctrinated in the belief that "only in America" can this new freedom work for the good of all. It is my personal opinion that abortion is not the answer, but that it will serve to stir the country to educate its free women and men in areas of birth control, sex, and health. This will take time, effort, and money.

It is not a problem of science, but a problem of humanities.

Mrs. Herndon, if I had not been so busy, I would have explained this to you. Your daughter-in-law had an abortion in the context of her own private decisions. She has the same right to her opinions as you do to yours. As for you, think about what you can do to help the public situation that you deplore. Don't pass the buck to doctors. Abortion, the Trojan Horse, is realistic and in the front yard.

CHAPTER THREE

The Abortion

The visitor to my office was not a patient but the daughter of a friend.

"I'm doing a paper on abortions." She smiled, embarrassed by the subject. "I can't find any real information, and Mother said you could help me."

It was a good social way to end a hard day, and I was pleased. The mechanics of abortion are not yet in the high schools, but the children are interested. Abortion is a fact of their language and thoughts.

I took a second look at my eager young friend with her poised pencil and new yellow legal pad. I decided that her report would be more accurate for her and less time-consuming for me if I typed it out at home. Besides, there were a few related facts that she needed to know before she learned the techniques of abortion.

I typed the facts and information that night and mailed

them to her, hoping that her professor would not be shocked and that her paper would be worth at least a "B." Here is what I said.

The Facts About Abortion

The pregnant person decides to have the abortion. If she is under twelve weeks gravid, there are many places where she can go. Planned Parenthood was one of the earliest volunteer agencies to accept the challenge of "every child a wanted child" and "children by choice." Its vision has always had an international base. This is obviously the way of answering the problems of overpopulation in the uneducated, poverty areas of the world. Abortion is the bludgeon weapon of population control and compares with the child exploitation of the past. Better weapons are birth control for women and vasectomies for men. Scientists are focusing on a better pill. The "morning after pill" and a "male pill" will be real breakthroughs. But research takes time and involved experimentation, as well as carefully scrutinized long-range effects. The tragic incidences of vaginal cancer in diethylstilbesterol (called DES by the public) serves as a warning of too hasty deductions and acceptance of a medicine that seemed harmless. Even now, some are pushing this DES for the "morning after" pill—in spite of the errors of twenty years ago. Science must proceed more slowly than the need.

The birth control battle is being waged at the high level of the United Nations. Mrs. Helvi Srpila of Finland, the first woman Assistant General, drafted the international "Study on the Inter-relationship of the Status of Women and Family Planning." The report states that countries which forbid family planning information and supply "are infringing on the exercise of basic human rights." It further says that there should be "new laws guaranteeing access to all relevant information, education, and services." The report stresses human rights to govern productive behavior. Confronted with the dire problems of over-population and dwindling food supplies, leaders of the world are listening and hearing the message because human suffering is acute.

Planned Parenthood

In our country, necessary steps are forming with a pattern for organizations that will soon be available in all areas. An excellent local Planned Parenthood agency serves my purpose of outline for a correct process that will effectively answer the need. This agency provides counseling procedure, operations, and recovery area. Birth control information including vasectomies for men is shared. Counseling is provided with options given. Abortions and vasectomies are performed by licensed doctors. There is a three week check-up after abortion. Birth control is stressed. Methods are explained repeatedly in the counseling procedure. Mental and emotional problems are referred to mental health centers as are medically related troubles. The program is effective and outlines the need.

In organizations like this, qualified personnel is of first importance. The doctors and counselors must be excel-

lent. There is the danger of assembly line treatment
inherent in any such program so every available precau-
tion should be taken to avoid this. The necessity for good
surgical treatment is obvious. Hasty physical examinations and superficial counseling are dangerous. The fee
for services should be nominal.

The Abortion

The patient is examined by a doctor to determine that
she is no further pregnant than her menstrual history
indicates. She is placed in a sterile operating room, draped
as in the television shows, and the vaginal area is further
sterilized. Some type of local or general anaesthesia is
used. An instrument is placed in the vagina to visualize
the cervix. The opening of the womb is grasped with a
double tooth instrument called a tenaculum to hold it in
place while the cervical dilators are used to open the
cervix large enough to allow a curette (a loop-shaped
cutting instrument) to be placed inside the womb. This
instrument is used to scrape the lining of the womb. It cuts
the foetus into bits and also removes the afterbirth (placenta). This is termed a D and C. If one looks he will see
parts of a hand, legs, head, or any other part of the body.
Gruesome? Yes! Factual? Yes!

The Suction Technique

This varies a little from the former. A hollow plastic
tube is pressed into the womb, and the products of conception are removed by negative pressure which dismem-

bers the foetus. The products are then sucked into a jar attached to the end of the tubing.

The patients do not see the removed foetuses, but it would certainly motivate them toward birth control if they did. I believe this aspect of the procedure should be introduced into the sex educational study. Many state highway departments require violators to view color films of fatal car accidents caused by speeders, carelessness, or drunken driving. The actual film causes fainting, vomiting, and better driving. It is similar to the action of killers who have a delayed conscience when they see the picture of their victims and the sadness of the family in the court rooms.

Amniotic Fluid Exchange, or Salting

This is a hospital procedure with sedation at times, and anaesthesia. This is often used from fourteen weeks pregnant to the end of the second trimester (or, roughly stated, nearing five months, plus or minus). The patient is taken to the operating room. She is draped as if she were going to have an abdominal operation. A six inch needle is introduced through the abdominal wall just below the navel. Some amniotic fluid is drawn off. This is the fluid the baby is suspended in, and if carried to near term, this is called by the laymen "the bag of waters." A concentrated salt solution is then introduced into the amniotic sac. This is usually about 200 cc's. (500 cc's is one pint.) The patient is allowed to remain in the hospital until a "spontaneous" labor starts, and then a vaginal delivery is done to the dead foetus. The average time from "salting" to expulsion of the foetus may vary from a few hours to several days. The injected solution kills the baby, and thus a dead foetus is expelled most of the time. There are more than just a few rare instances where a living baby has been expelled but soon to die after birth. More about the size of these babies later. If they breathe and have a heartbeat, they may be declared as an income tax deduction as a "dependent."

The complications have been everything from the rare death of the mother to several weeks of hospitalization due to physical complications.

Prostaglandin substitution for the salt solution has been introduced, and much study has been done on the difference or possible advantages of this. Of academic interest may be a report from the New York Academy of Medicine, section on obstetrics and gynecology, supported in part by a grant of one of the larger drug houses. The conclusion at this 1974 symposium was that PGF has had "a possible advantage over saline abortion."

Many times the placenta is not expelled in these cases, and the doctor has to explore the uterus. This is done by inserting his entire hand into the uterus. The tissue involved is worked away from the lining of the womb.

Many of these foetuses cry and breathe until they die from prematurity. They are perfectly formed babies. They have all the functioning organs, even several physical elements that mother's ask when a premature baby is born. "Can you tell me if it was a boy or a girl? Did it have fingernails and hair?" The obvious answer is, YES. A nineteen week foetus is visually different from a full-term baby only in size. The skin is "shiny" but it looks like a baby and is a baby. The products of "convenient" abortions indict females.

Hysterotomy

This is akin to a Caesarean section. The major operation is done through an abdominal incision through the uterus. The foetus is removed along with the placenta. If future babies are desired, a like operation is in order for the full-term infant. The hospital stay is about one week for this.

Hysterectomy

This is a procedure where not only the foetus but the uterus (or "baby carriage") is removed. The surgical complications are increased, and there are deaths from this. The baby usually doesn't cry or breathe as the uterus isn't opened after removal until the products of conception have died. This is obviously a major operation, and ten days of hospitalization is average.

Nurses' Attitudes toward Abortion

The nurse, like the doctor, has been trained to save and serve human life. I believe that this is a calling, stimulated by compassion for and a desire to help humanity. This is instilled by training, but it is more. It is a talent and a facet of her personality. Nurses who assist on abortions in controlled hospitals (abortions done for the mother's health: heart disease, diabetes, and such, as well as because of gene studies) often develop a negative attitude about being an assistant on these cases. Most hospitals do not demand that a certain nurse must take her rotation turn in "scrubbing" with the doctor in these indicated cases. Her reaction is often akin to the distress and repugnance of the child who sees the dead baby bird, kitten, or puppy. Only this is a baby. A report from Hawaii stated that many nurses experienced a delayed (six months to two years) psychological problem after routine service on abortion cases.

Summary of Methods to Interrupt Pregnancy

The methods below may vary a week or so with different abortionists, but the general idea is as follows:

Early pregnancy—to 13 weeks

They are generally equally divided between the D and C method and the suction or vacuum technique. Local or general anaesthesia is usually preferred.

13 weeks to 28 weeks

This also is a variable among operators. They choose the salting technique or hysterotomy, or sometimes hysterectomy.

From thirteen weeks pregnant plus, patients are usually hospitalized. General anaesthesia as a rule.

DEFINITIONS**

Pregnant	With child: gravid
Premature	Occurring before the proper time
Miscarriage	Expulsion of the foetus before it is viable
Viable	That stage of development that will permit the foetus to live outside of the uterus
Abortion	Miscarry: bring forth a non-viable foetus
	Expulsion of the products of conception before the child is viable. When this occurs within the first three months, it is called an abortion: from this time to viability, it is called immature delivery ˙or miscarriage—and from the period of viability to full term —premature delivery
Aborticide	Killing of an unborn foetus—the agent which destroys the foetus and produces abortion.

**Above definitions from *Blakiston's Illustrated Medical Dictionary, Second Edition*.

Zygote	The fertilized ovum before cleavage
Cleavage	An early stage of the process of development between the fertilization and the blastula
Blastula	A round mass consisting of a central cavity surrounded by layers of cells produced by the cleavage of the ovum

Ovum	A cell of the mother's body—not an independent life
Sperm	A cell of the father's body—it has reached the end point of its maturity
Fertilized ovum	A combination of the sperm and the ovum. It contains all the chromosomes and genes the baby will have if allowed to reach maturity. About one week after fertilization, (which takes place in the Fallopian tube of the female) it implants within the wall of the inside of the uterus.

When does the heart of the foetus begin to beat?

This has been traced on E.K.G.'s at nine weeks. A fetone often allows the prospective mother and doctor to hear this at eleven weeks if the patient's abdominal wall isn't too thick.

Early activities of the foetus:

9-10 weeks the foetus swallows, squints, and moves the tongue
11-12 weeks the foetus is sucking the thumb
11-12 weeks if one strokes the palm, the foetus makes a fist
11-15 weeks the foetus has fingernails and eyelashes
11 weeks the foetus has all of its systems working
13 weeks—In 1974, the discovery was made for the first

time that the foetus began to breathe at various rates and on various occasions. This discovery is factual.

Weight of the foetus:

12 weeks—about one ounce
15 weeks—about six ounces
20 weeks—about one pound
40 weeks (full term)—five pounds (plus)

Part Two: Problems

Present problems of which the person considering abortion should be aware.

CHAPTER FOUR

Communication

Juanita and her mother were sitting in my office crying. Juanita was fourteen and pregnant. She was not from rape and the ghetto; she was from innocence, family love, and private schools.

"I never thought this would happen to us. Why didn't she talk to me?" her mother half sighed, half asked. And as she turned to leave she whispered, "Warn your young mothers that this can happen to the best of parents; they just don't know. They just don't know."

How do you warn parents? Do you really need to tell them that their young children are living in a revolution-ary world? It's not all Cokes, ruffled potato chips, and loud music. It is not in the least like the world the adults have known. Parent awakening is necessary, and so is sex education for children. The young toss out pietistic phrases like "Lack of communication," "Who am I?" and

"What's your hangup?" These are used as major indict-
ments against the whole race of parents. Father's first
reaction to these trite phrases is generally predictable.
He wishes he could find some square little corner in
semiseclusion—and vomit. "Lack of communication!" he
shouts. "Well, I've talked till I'm hoarse! She (he) won't
listen."

The "Who am I?" emits a strained voicing of, "I'll tell
her (him) she's a lazy radical." The "What's your hangup?" elicits a tirade against dirty jeans, too-long or too-
short dresses for girls, and long hair for boys. If the
young are still in the room, Father's temper will overflow
into the abstractions behind "stupid protest marches"
and weird "causes." It is reminiscent of Archie Bunker
and his scream of, "Why don't you bathe? Are you a
Commie?"

So Father speaks harshly and emotionally to one he
deeply loves, and the dividing line between them becomes
a gulf. He had plans for his child. His plans. He selected
dolls or brought home footballs, and laughed about that
Linus security blanket when they were toddlers. He
worried when they were sick and dreaded the bad side
effects from immunizations. He sacrificed and did everything he could. And where is he now? His child is a
stranger and seems to be speaking in a foreign tongue.
Father's feelings are not just hurt; they are smashed. He
may understand the words the child says, but he can't
hear the meaning. He moves in an atmosphere of the
lonely sound of a guitar or the recorded noise of the
latest musical craze. These last are accompanied by words
and phrases that seem poetry to the young but are mean-

ingless, nonsense sounds to the father. Mother doesn't feel much better, but Father is the epitome of frustration.

Where Do We Start?

To better understand their foreign language and response to our stimulations, we need to get several facts into perspective. Our children fall into the basic definition found in *Webster's Dictionary:* "Adolescence is that period from puberty to maturity." Puberty is the age when it is possible to beget or bear children. Fourteen years in boys, and twelve years in girls. The word maturity is the iron curtain to reasonable thinking. It's too sad that they can't sign up for maturity like they sign up for scouting and swimming lessons, but maturity isn't gained by steady numerical promotion from grade to grade. It grows like a tree by way of devious branches and leaves, and it should be a growing situation until we die. The generation gap is caused in part by stagnant parents. The aware parent gains in wisdom and maturity via his child.

Now it is definitely reasonable to think that at puberty the teenager should not start begetting humans; however, his hormones and sexual development are ready for reproduction. The society in the United States rebels at the thought of teenagers giving birth to young. They lack what we like to call "social maturity." In many cases, the young have tried to overcome this stigma by marriage. The divorce courts show that about seventy-five percent of teenage marriages end in divorce.

To illustrate the complexities with which our young

are faced, we can further review the hormonal content of the human body as compared to mammals. A house pet gives birth, and within a few months, the young are independent enough to leave the mother and start a reproductive cycle all their own. No one tells them "no" or "don't." The owners usually face the problem of giving the young produced by their pets to friends letting them bother with the population increase.

But human beings are not house pets.

The Culture Has Changed

Parents claim that the situation today is no different than when they were young, but this is simply not realistic. The hormones are the same, but the culture is vastly different. Just as there aren't too many Puritan families around in the parent generation, there aren't too many Tom Sawyers and Pollyannas in the youth generation. Parents discuss sex in terms of "No," or give the young a complete ivory-covered silence with a theological halo. We shouldn't always say "yes and yes," but we should recognize the difference between their world and temptations in it. Parents should listen intelligently.

And then there are the adolescents who don't try to communicate. They want to believe that there is no mutual ground for understanding, fearing that we will infantize them. But children weren't born this way. How incessantly they talked when they were young! How often did they ask, "Why?" How often were we watching the mentally constipating television when they came in bright-eyed to ask a personally important question? "Don't walk in front of the television," has become as much of a household phrase as "It's raining." We negate most of the very young's ideas with the subconscious feeling that children should be seen and not heard. This is done in everything. Mother is busy in the kitchen. Daddy is tired and will "explain that later." On and on go the brush-offs.

As the child approaches puberty, this lack of communication is a second nature to both sides—parents and children. Of course, if there is a serious illness, bad report card from school, or some such crisis, the communication gets to a "gut" level. Children and adolescents don't "cotton" to gut level talking on this every now and then schedule. This is communication? Parents comment on the news, TV reports, and daily incidences, and this is often of a negative nature. "That politician is a crook." "Our foreign aid is helping a bunch of cutthroats." "That movie star must be a pervert." "Serves him right to be shot." "The whole world is rotten." This last phrase is often a summation of our total attitude toward world events. The adolescent goes into the schoolyard and the streets with the impression that the world is rotten. He has been programmed to this and acts accordingly.

So with a body full of hormones, he goes into the "rotten" world that we have clearly, yet semiconsciously, defined for him. He looks through his parents' eyes at first. However, he basically wants one thing; he wants to be accepted by his peer group. This acceptance is based upon externals such as hair, dress, and responses to peers. The internals are those worrisome hormones and a feeling of dependency. The latter is usually to the family, but it is frequently disguised by a wall of silence.

In the world of pets, animal independence is reached

at "animal puberty," and they are as mature as they will ever be. They are on their happy way. Our children? No. They have to struggle through at least eight (usually more) years of being physically mature and mentally immature. This eight year interval is where most parents will meet their biggest problems. This was not as true in the safety of our own adolescent days, but it is true today. We need all of the maturity of our accumulated years. Our children have a long canoe, but not much of a paddle and not much experience. They need us. We can't leave them to drown. It's not love's way nor is it the way of happiness, peace of mind, or duty. It is true that adolescents are often rebellious, irresponsible, and selfish with a pompous, oily idealism that seems without humor. But on the other side of the coin, the love, earnestness, and youthful exuberance are genuine.

What Are the Values?

And what are the values that we have passed on to our children? The compactness of our living conditions allow for few secrets. Look at the facts. They are seeking to learn. They can't stand by in family arguments as though Mother and Daddy were speaking Chinese. They aren't solidly dull. They are listening, and they will identify with one side or the other and try to understand. Their security depends on it. Theirs is a sharp cornered world in which they must safely bounce and slide. Look at some more facts. Father often discusses a "slick" business deal in which he outsmarted another, and he laughs about a sly income tax deduction. An insurance claim to the car may be a good business deal because Father cracked the windshield while driving into the garage, but he tells the insurance adjustor that a flying rock from a large gravel truck hit it. Mother tells the phone caller, "He's at the office. Did you try to reach him there?" In reality Father is a very few feet away engrossed in a football game on television. Mother tells Father's boss that he's too sick to come to work, but he's really sleeping off a hangover. The preadolescent or adolescent heard both parents come in the night before. There were the halting footsteps of Daddy, and the unguarded language when he missed a step in the dark. These things seep into the young and impressionable mind, but the youth learns not to ask questions or make comments until the next day. A tape recording of such incidents would shock the parents involved. The language, the tone of voice, and the implications are harsh and traumatic experiences to the young.

They Learn by Example

Then there are other little things. Daddy sees a friend in the drug store, and together they eye the nubile clerk behind the counter. They gaze at her frontal display assets. They nudge each other and smile. But this isn't all. They will make a few male-type comments that Child will hear, and there is the moral interpretation that it's all right because Daddy talks like that. Do our children need the old Gestapo techniques to gather information? Of course not. They are exposed to it in a spidery form, and their brain cells are pulsating, and their hormones coiled. Children can't live in the blankness of a moonscape, but it's often hard to find the security of values in the reality of their world.

How many children, fresh and eager from hygiene class, have dashed home to tell Mother and Daddy that they must stop smoking and drinking? They are armed with statistics, new knowledge, missionary zeal, and love. They are sincere; they have the undeniable book facts. It would be interesting to know how many parents change their habits because their children tell them such habits are unhealthy and death-dealing.

When parents turn the coin and berate their children for smoking, drinking, and sexing, they should think back to the examples they set as a basis for self-discipline and behavior. If our children seem pitifully unskilled in decision-making, how many of us can throw stones? They say they don't like our world. The dichotomy of our reasoning and behavior is too great because it has a double standard of discipline and behavior—one for them, and one for us. Theirs is more than a frown type resentment; it's a heavy resentment against the phrase, "Don't do as I do; do as I say."

Parents do try, and they do love their children. There is no way to be perfect. There is no way to get out of Babylon. It might help if we could play the guitar, and it would be great to have the resilience of youth; they can bounce back with enthusiasm and high hopes while we are still licking our wounds in a daze. But our only hope is in coping on a day-to-day basis in the psychedelic world of the young.

And where do they get some of their other values?

There is television, and we are in our first generation of influence of this medium. Harassed mothers say, "Why don't you watch a program?" They have a choice of the Peyton Place sex variety or police stories with crime and violence, interspersed with commercial gems of, "Mother never told me about white teeth," and, "I must be kissable." Their values are formed in a wilderness of good and bad, right and wrong.

Then there are movies and pornography. In the world of adolescence, it's certainly not all Walt Disney. Sex is seldom subtly portrayed on film, but even when it is, it is not missed by bright-eyed, eager youths with the pulsating hormones. The examples are set, and there is understanding. Abnormal porno books are easily obtainable, and with the young, it is a reaching out for necessary information. It has to do with the insatiable hunger for what goes on in the world. Daddy has had copies of *Playboy,* and the difference is only one of degree. Does he leave it on the coffee table? Not usually. But often he leaves it on the bedside table. Sometimes it can be found on the same shelf as the Bible. The magazines probably show more usage than the crisp, unread pages of the Bible.

And sometimes there is the influence of the church; but the church speaks of budgets, parking lots, and social gospel. But the Bible says, "Pray and the Lord will provide." It promises a personal relationship with God, and if the heart of man is with Him, the rightness of society will follow. The preacher often tries, but the facts of life seem to be that he must please his deacons and his congregation before he listens to the Word and to the

Holy Spirit. He may be plagued with his own clay feet. One of my Episcopal patients told me that her young son was an acolyte and made a small error in his serving of communion. After a brilliant sermon on keeping your cool, and loving your neighbor, the rector found the time and energy to berate the boy furiously for his mistake. The incident had a traumatic effect on the boy. The young can see through the darkness like owls.

So the young are captured into society in adolescence with some judgments from vicarious living and as much personal wisdom as is possible in the thirteen year span that encompasses everything from toilet training to gamesmanship. Any book that claims to be an exacting guide toward dealing with any human behavior or mental flagellation is certainly written by one who possibly needs more help than the reader. But some smattering of experiences, both personal and professional, do give one some pertinent points that may be helpful in establishing a few ground rules. Perhaps each individual parent can build his or her game plan on this basis, using the individuality of those involved to open the communication lines.

Adults Have Responsibilities

We are adults. Remember the dictionary—adolescence lasts from puberty to maturity. We are supposed to be mature. Even in the preschool age, we should not sell the children short in the question and answer department. Obviously, the housewife shouldn't burn the bacon to answer a question; she should calmly explain why she is postponing the dialogue a few minutes. The young can reason and can compromise with time. Besides the dialogue, we should listen when the child talks. Most of us are tuned in to other adults, but when the very young come to tell us something—the brush off. And a nail is put into the door of silence. Every parent says over and over, "Don't interrupt." The tone of voice adds several exclamation points. Do you consider how little time you really listen and how much less time the child has to get a word into your busy world? An objective mind can see this clearly. If necessary, make certain periods of the morning, afternoon, and early evening available for discussions. A point in case is the story of the little girl who tried to tell her mother that some man was in their car. The mother was engaged in a very long phone conversation and gave her the "go away" treatment. In an hour, the mother looked out the window and was startled to see that her car was gone. The cry, "Mummy, I told you some man was getting in our car," caused a tirade against the child because she hadn't been more emphatic. Listen! Have definite scheduled times for discussion which both you and the child can agree upon.

The babble of the preschooler, is often followed by the silence of the juvenile. At this age, he is apt to buzz through the house like a fly. He eats, and he rests and speaks in monosyllables. "What kind of a day did you have at school?" elicits this response, "Same as always." Or sometimes it is only a shrug. The question like "Was that John who walked home with you?" earns a what-does-it-matter-to-you expression. What does it matter to you? It matters, and your love turns somersaults in your stomach as your mouth opens and closes without words. The trick is making him realize that you care but stopping before the "nag" sets in.

The Adolescent and You

Books and books have been written about this problem. The salient facts are only a few. If the first issue described above is observed, the adolescent may be more accessible to you and vice versa.

SOME DON'T'S

Don't criticize every mod movie or show on television. (Your child dresses like some of the actors, and she or he knows this is a projection on your part.)
Don't try to act their age in speech or manner. (You are different in experience and point of time.)
Don't stare at their hair or dress.

I met my son at the airport after he had played in one of the New Year's Bowl games. I hadn't seen him eyeball to eyeball in weeks. My words of praise were lost on his ears. I was looking at the length of his hair, and he could see that and only that. We had a polite conversation until we arrived home. After he kissed his mother, she glued her eyes to his hair—unconsciously—and small pleasantries were exchanged under more than tension. The next morning at breakfast, I stared at the hair again. Bop and Boom. The communication door was shut.

The same eye appraisal applies to too long (or too short) dresses. After many months, I have learned to do a trick that an ex-convict explained to me years ago. This rehabilitated gentleman told me that in most prisons there was a silent contest in their day-to-day contact between the inmates and the guards to see who could outstare the other. The convicts always won. How? They never looked the guard in the eye but stared intently at the bridge of the guard's nose. The guard couldn't differentiate the exact point of the focus, and his eyes would invariably wander first. This will stand you in good stead in confronting people with disabilities, as well as your own children.

My mother almost tried this one time when our minister came for a visit. The gentleman had a very, very big nose. I was warned not to stare at this facial overendowment. After pouring coffee, Mother asked if he wanted NOSE in his coffee. I've heard comics use this joke, but I was there when it happened.

MORE DON'T'S

Don't criticize their friends.
Don't use the words hippie, in-group, or any other like expressions. (You obviously mean it derogatorily, and they know it.)
Don't minimize a conflict they bring to you. (Try to give it a good ear and not too fluent tongue. Most of the time they want you to listen. They are still dependents—remember? And this enforces the security of knowing where they can turn if real problems arise.)

"Bad manners and morals of the young" is a phrase that most middle-aged parents will agree upon. Is this new? No! It was said by Aristotle some two thousand years ago.

Most of us view our older progeny as children. We know they are grown, and if there is doubt, we can look it up legally and read the paper that states that they are men and women at the age of eighteen years. The "we know best" parent profile is our way of attempting to keep complete control and shuts the door to most communication. We can't make a cold statement and generalize. We need adept magical formulas to handle the question. We must deal from strength toward moulding strength. Many older teenagers need and want our positiveness in direction. It gives them security and saves them from the pangs of decision. But there is one solid ultimatum. Don't say "do this or do that" because you close the door to all options. Your pride and your child's pride are on the line, and both are options. The "either-or" world is a wretchedly lonely one. Remember that it is maturity's weapon of strength to rock with the boat, and duck with the punches. Even a few years is not much compared to losing your child. Live day by day. If you are a God family—pray. Pray a lot. The "do this or else" mandate is rejection. Pride and stubbornness (usually father and child) are real rocks. We frequently close the door in love. It's a closed door with broken hearts, and there is little chance of opening it. Runaways and youthful suicides stand as witnesses to the difficulty of backtracking from this position. Parents and children are not readily replaceable; so the knife is double-edged. Dictatorial mandates leave us no options.

The twelve to sixteen group isn't very eager for Mother's and Father's advice on anything—but most especially sex. Education must come by way of the school and church or any other facsimile that offers value of reason, responsibility, and ethical mores.

So your daughter is pregnant and unmarried, and she tells you because she needs money for an abortion. The involved boy is safely in his room at his home playing his guitar or zooming his motorbike around the neighborhood. Hopefully he is concerned.

He certainly didn't exploit your daughter. It is just that exploitation facilities are built-in. Sex is the method that animals and plants reproduce their kind. The flower is the sexual organ of the plant. For humans, sex is more than a physical problem. It is involved with moral teachings and tense psychological problems. At the moment your daughter announces that she is pregnant, the world falls apart. Often Mother's first instinct is "What will your daddy say?" and "What will the family and neighbors think?" Your thoughts are often not altruistic.

If communication had been present, possibly your daughter might have avoided the pregnancy, or at the least, she would have come to you at the first thought of trouble.

Parents, communication is a discipline for you in the early years of your child's life. But later it is your lifeline to them. Parents should try to up-date and try to be fair, as well as to grow and change with their children and society. Remember that even with absolutes, there is always forgiveness and love.

CHAPTER FIVE

To Marry or Not to Marry

"But my boyfriend wants me to have an abortion. He has just started his own band. It's his big chance!" Vivian was nineteen, vivacious, and beautiful. She was also pregnant.

"Bring him to see me, and we'll talk it through," I suggested.

"He won't want to come," she said honestly. "I'm not really the rose-covered cottage marrying type either, but this is different—the pregnancy and everything. I guess it's really just my decision."

Sex is basic. In these days of holy and unholy word wars about sex, this fact still seems incontestable. It is sex that will maintain it. It is true that men have subjugated women, but the opposite is also true. Feminists often blame God, Eve, and the Pope on the exploitation of women. But logical reasoning has to extend past theological cultures into other and more primitive times. Had human reproduction been a matter of laying eggs and slithering away like fish, men and women might have built a great variety of social patterns inspired by only individual differences and cultures. As things are, the family is as fundamental to civilization as shelter. This is true even if one leaves religious teaching out of the picture, as in the following.

It wasn't the male who instigated the family unit. It was the biology of Woman and female wiles appealing to man's compassion. Man later became less childlike and shrewdly contrived to make Woman the servant of the world, but his initial gesture was one of altruism. Originally, man lacked books on sex and knew only that Woman was mysteriously subject to childbearing. Man thought that maybe pregnancy had something to do with the moon, sun, or trees. In the meantime, Woman was forever carrying babies in her arms, her body, or both. Gestation was long, birth difficult, and the feeding of the young was a chore. Woman could starve this way. Additionally, the food supply was uncertain. There were huge tigers around the rocks and snakes on the ground, not even to mention obvious hazards like hostile tribes and bad weather. Woman looked around, and there was Man—happy, strong, and dancing. He was the obvious answer to the quest for security of herself and her young. If Man could supply her needs, Woman would not need to kill or leave her young. Woman was no different from the fowls of the air or the beasts of the fields in that she had an instinct for her young plus the human element called love.

Where has this picturesque scene gone in this Age of Abortion? God or nature, depending upon your allegiance, not only gave Woman reproductive power but also a motivation to live. Now Woman eyed the situation. She recognized that the sun, moon, and the trees couldn't get the job done. She reasoned that man could be induced to supply sustenance, and if so, life would be better. Now Man had an inbuilt thing called a sex drive, and Woman offered great satisfaction in that direction; he also felt a strange compassion for Woman and her young. This proved that he too was human and felt loving concern. He agreed to share his food with Woman and her young. Here we have the birth of the family and subsequent male domination. Man became lord and master because of this evolutionary process.

And then came knowledge of how babies were made. Certainly Woman must have figured out this one, and Man refused to believe it for hundreds of years. Primitive man surely had the same "who, me?" attitude so prevalent today. That boyish look of innocence must be inherent in the species. Man liked the one about the sun, moon, and trees. It was probably many long years before he admitted parenthood, but truth has a way of asserting itself. And then came the discipline of maternity. In order to identify his own flesh and blood, man needed assurance of the fidelity of the mother. He didn't want to feed his friends' children, too. Except for these elementary facts of reproduction, men and women might live in a vastly greater variety of social patterns, just as they are attempting to do today. But it is always Woman who is the loser.

Necessity for the Family

And so we have the family as a social unit based on the biological facts of procreation. Now the marriage ceremony doesn't make Woman any more monogamous than Man; it is every woman's secret that she is readily attracted to other men. Although sexual equality and woman's small liberation will right many wrongs, Woman still knows that the family as a fundamental unit is a most convenient way to rear children. And more than this, it's fairly basic to animal instinct. The law of nature that provides love and desire for the young is deep within Woman, and she is not apt to abdicate that law for waterbeds, alpaca rugs and the living *Playgirl* centerfold. Today's educated, childless persons fill the value with a variety of pets like cats, dogs, and hamsters, which only reaffirms in a negative fashion the ageold story of the innate desire for reproduction and love of the young.

Pregnancies out of marriage are not outmoded moralities; it is just that they are as impractical today as they were in primitive times. We can have a sexual revolution, but there will never be a paralleling reproductive revolution. Woman begets; this is an irrefutable fact. Art, literature, movies, television, and jokes to the contrary, Woman was born knowing that even the birds and the bees have a prescribed pattern of conformity in the family, and anything less is degrading. If modern woman feels constrained to test and feel sex, she should surely have the good sense to go prepared. Prevention is smart; cure is rough. Or, plainer yet, the pill is smart; abortion is rough. To say that modern woman will swap the joys of family and home for the thrilling but fleeting joys of sex is to say that primitive woman was smarter than educated woman. When maturity sets in, women will tire of the dance and settle for home—and so will men.

And we have been talking about man and woman. The real danger lies with boy and girl. But how old was primitive man and woman? They were the originators of the family unit. Our young dancers are idealistic and chase their butterflys without a net. They will learn, and time is on their side. Parents hold tight to patience and love. Times are confusing, and we as parents are hypocrites. Fathers cheat in many ways and often mothers do, too. But youth will rediscover the same old basics and pick up the pattern again. Hopefully, with a stronger warp and woof.

CHAPTER SIX

These are the 70s

Ms. Thomason and her daughter Dot sat in my office in a state of family fury.

"I found these pills in her drawer; they are birth control pills—aren't they?" She placed two nondescript pills on my desk.

They could have been vitamins, I supposed, wondering what Dot had told her mother. She and I both knew that they were birth control pills. "I'm not a pharmacist," I said, noticing Dot's frown disappear.

"She's just seventeen, but she's with this boy morning, noon, and night," her mother emphasized disapprovingly.

"I need to talk with you two separately," I said. "Dot, suppose you wait in the reception room a little while. Don't worry, if those pills are helping you, stay with them regularly," I added not wanting her to think that I would betray her. I reluctantly turned to Ms. Thomason.

What do you say to a mother who was a young girl way back in the 1950s? If she had known anything about birth control pills, she wouldn't have taken them out of the container for diagnosis. Those pills and that container need to stay together.

Poor Ms. Thomason. I wondered if I could get past her righteous indignation and into her reason. The family had had quite a battle. They had probably attacked Dot with a whole battalion of religious morals. I was not going to expose Dot's pills, but I did have a few things to say to her mother. Would she vote for a pregnant unmarried daughter or a seventeen year old pregnant married daughter? If she took her daughter off the pills, this was probably her choice. The time for additional moral training was just about gone.

A discourse on the birds and the bees will not follow because even a scientist doesn't get much when he puts a bird and a bee together. However, from some professional insight and experience, I can suggest several attitudes toward sex and adolescence which may help.

Most young girls are not like Dot, but most mothers, like Dot's, are innocent about their daughter's sexual advancement. They always say that hormones are the same as when they were young, and nature doesn't change. True. But hormones are unmarked and traceless. Surface listening won't get it but will help. If your daughter refuses pizza and dashes to the bedroom in a state of sobs-for-no-reason, the traceless hormones are at work. The human social side to hormones is a big factor, and mother can probably think back but *times have* changed.

Stimulations differ radically from the 50s. Both mother and daughter will have a more difficult time if mother doesn't accept this.

We have defined the period of adolescence from puberty to maturity as the period when one's reasoning catches up with physical development. These are the problem years. The young girl gets guidance through this conflicting and disturbing period from several factions: (1) family, (2) peers, and (3) community.

During the adolescent years, Mother needs to be awake. Wide awake. Complicating the hormone situation is the fact that the daughter is entirely different at home than in a crowd of peers. Her surface pattern and internal pattern are two different things. Her guidance will come from Mother, peers and community. The latter includes school, church and entertainment. As for Mother, she is usually the family figure. Father is occasionally the image, or if there is a glamorous big sister or brother, they can help, but it's really Mother's job. No matter how interested she is in golf, work, or committees, she needs to put Daughter at the top of the calendar. This is no time to develop a permissive streak.

That first menstruation means that the emotional drives are on "go." Too often Mother is only concerned about the possible pain that Daughter has with these first menses. "I hope you won't cramp as I did," is the same trite thing as telling a child not to put beans up the baby's nose. The seed has been planted about pain, and she is more likely to have it. If she has pain and the pattern continues, take her to a gynecologist. The physical reasons can often be helped by oral hormones. They are the same as birth control pills and usually control pain as well as regulating periods.

The hormonal changes in menstruation which affect her entire personality are rarely mentioned. The fact that the female child with the mature body who is living in the family is an unmentionable subject is taking her back to the Dark Ages. We can't use a guideline for every daughter, but we can try. Give her options for discussion, as well as stimulation and questioning. Maybe you can't be an explainer of hormones and boy-girl relationships like some people are dancers, singers, and linguists, but you can update. You can have insight and pass it along. Gradually, after the first menstruation, you can expect your daughter to withdraw into a shell, covered with the ratio of the changing estrogen-progesterone battle. She won't think that anyone over the age of twenty will understand her, but a scattering of books around the house relating to teen problems may raise her opinion of you. It is normal for her to feel mentally superior, so don't be surprised or defensive. The venomous scorn of the young can be very character building for you. The honest fact is that she may be more knowledgeable at fifteen than you are at thirty-five or older.

It is hard for mothers to realize the depth of change in society. You may still be fighting sex education in schools. Many are. Your child may indeed be an innocent in a protected world, but college or something akin to it is next on the scene. Prepare her. Don't rest in the moral shock of "whatever is happening to the world today?" You must try. Go to the local library. Read books on sex and the teenagers; look in the card files and ask the librarian about new books on teen guidance. Prefer selections written recently, not in the fifties or early sixties. Few of the older studies anticipated the crises of the seventies. Mothers get with it; it won't go away like measles. Don't rely on how it was before you were married because even five years ago life was not the same. Your child doesn't have a rubber backbone; temptations are served on a silver platter. An informed parent is the only one who has a chance of communication.

If there is a totally unsatisfactory communication, outside counseling or psychotherapy is practical. Sometimes the teenager's withdrawal or attack stems from a major depression. Studies show that there is a high incidence of this in the adolescent bracket; it drops off in the twenty year plus age-group. The facts are not established as yet, but this may be caused by a hormone imbalance and monthly cyclic changes. Overt behavior patterns which hide real depressions are frequently not recognized by the family as serious emotional problems. This can be a sign of real trouble.

The combustion of hormones in a changed society is enough but is not the total picture. All of the errors of parenthood and faulty discipline come to the front. The effects of over-discipline, indifference or over-protectiveness blast out. Mother may need to be more than a fast reader to work her daughter out of this corner. Environmental factors such as problems with others in the family, lack of affection, and even friend or teacher rejection may also join in the general crisis.

So there are many major reasons for the mistakes of

teens which may be manifested by everything from over-eating to open rebellion against family, school, and sex. It is important to recognize the signs. If you don't have the answers for these major problems (which you usually don't), at least consult the family doctor or facsimile of same. Pregnancy, abortion, drugs, drinking, suicide, and runaways can result from neglect. It is not just one of those things that will go away.

Should a mother encourage her daughter to take birth control pills? Is this causing us to have further enrollees in the school of free love? There are no pat answers for this. If the mother and daughter are really on the same line, some compromise pleasing to both may be reached. If your case is like Ms. Thomason, you need to discuss the situation with your daughter in a realistic fashion. It's often better to leave Father out. Unless he's a bonafide liberal, he hasn't been crusading for female rights. It's better to educate him first and inform him later.

Our children are our most treasured possessions. Possessions? Of course not. Don't desert them when they need you the most. Rantings and ravings with "I told you so's" are impractical and destructive. Keep the lines open, and there will be a great reduction in these problems. Listen and listen again. We give our infant all the vaccines, but in the most trying time of her life, there is no sex immunization. Put your pride under the covers and try again. Be a martyr? No. Be a good parent.

Peer Group: The news about abortion has even seeped down to the kindergarten set. They listen to the news, too, and proponents of abortion have done everything but drop leaflets by plane. While women demand equality of sex, the males are right there cheering. Young girls inherit this freedom for which women fight. They have the sexual freedom, without their parents' approval, but with their peer approval. They have a right to their bodies; if they become pregnant, they have the right to an abortion. They know that the word "abortion" gives them their unpregnant bodies again, but it still is not a simple or uncomplicated affair. The girl is the total of her mental and physical capacity, environment, education, and cultural status. In spite of being uniquely herself and uniquely different, she wants peer approval. Who wants to go through life a virgin? The boyfriend isn't in there whispering, "Honey, the social world needs moral preservation," and he isn't saying, "Sex is great, but morals are mental peace—your mental peace." He's just whistling, riding his wheels around, and thinking great thoughts like: "Chastity has been replaced by fidelity." The male's web has been in the spinning stage a long time, and the last spin involves early going steady, abortion, and home is where the bed is.

Nobody mentions all the women who haven't had sex and don't miss it. In fact, it's something most women can learn about in five minutes when the right time comes. And if the right time never comes—so what? You don't see too many girls dancing around shouting about how sex happy they are. Boys—yes! Girls—no.

If our teenager gets pregnant without a marriage contract to hinder her, where is she? Hinder? She doesn't seem to realize that the contract is her protection. She usually must tell her parents and reestablish some kind of line of communication in this family emotionally-

formed storm. No double standards? That's what she
and her older sisters have been fighting for. Right?
Wrong. Where is the other member of the coital partnership? He's at home listening to his tapes. Sure, he hopes
she gets okay again, but his body hasn't been changed by
the intercourse that finds her pregnant.

So the young girl is placed in society with all the
hormones pulsating with a free tag attached to each
ovulating ovary. This girl is free. She is going into the
world of parked cars and the battle of the sexes with
peer approval as the victory, even though it may be only
a temporary win. The sad fact is that she does not have
any ammunition for the battle. She does not have the
correct knowledge of the motivation of ninety-nine percent of all post puberty males—sexual gratification and
forget the end results. An old un-Polish proverb is
that a male in tumescence has no conscience.

Peer approval needs medical and educational up-
dating, too; if there are to be early sex relations, there
should be birth control. Girls too often accept ridiculous
gossip about "the pill." They believe it causes everything
from cancer to three-headed babies in later life. Girls
like this belong in the primitive society. If they have
sexual intercourse without adequate birth control, they
will most certainly become pregnant sooner or later,
unless they are totally sterile which is not likely. They
should try to avoid an abortion. They should search for
advice. There are many available places like government
health agencies, and doctor's offices. They should not
trust the boyfriend for this information. Each girl is re-

sponsible for her own sense of liberty. Birth control is inexpensive, but abortion is costly financially, physically, and emotionally.

The Community

School: The responsibility of the school is sex education with all the ramifications of family, social, and moral elements. This will be mentioned later and repeated in this book. However, it should be noticed that small school rap sessions with a psychologist in attendance are a great additional approach. School monies are always difficult, so perhaps this is a job for PTA and a concerned community to promote, along with the usual drug information. More and more psychologists seem to be needed in the educational world. The field of psychology will stir more actively in this direction in the future. There has been a void for too long. The increasing teenage pregnancies emphasize this.

The Church: So many distressed mothers say, "And she always went to Sunday School and church." She didn't get pregnant in church; you can be sure of that. And the churches don't approve, but some speak out louder than others. Watching youth should not be a spectator sport for them either. The Sunday School and Sunday night youth groups could use some blood transfusions. If the congregation is looking for prospective Christians, the young are the most conveniently located; but church pictures showing the strong Moses holding those stone tablets of "Thou Shalt Not's" won't get the job done. And neither will those tired adults who volunteer for the teaching and helping jobs. There are lots of laborers in the vineyards, but you don't see much joy. And you don't hear much laughter, because nothing much is happening.

The worse enemies of vital faith are those who try to cut the Word to the times. If faith is to have relevance to its followers, as opposed to ethical mores and morals, the times must renovate to fit the Word. The Bible says that God is unchanging; His Word must also be unchanging.

Exciting new youth movements like the Fellowship of Christian Athletes, Campus Crusaders, Young Life, and various Jesus movements are reaching out to fill the vacuum. Mothers, get with it; don't be denominationally bound standpatters. Explore the possibilities. Talk with some of the new breed Christians.

Entertainment: The movies—the young don't go to see "The Life of Donald Duck" anymore. With all those X-rated films around, why should they?

There is not much point in discussing entertainment. It's everywhere, but much of it doesn't produce either great or stimulating ideas, if you happen to be looking for that sort of thing.

"Mothers, beware of the Horse." This is a big subject to discuss in a few pages, but my basic thought is only that there is no excuse for a mother's innocence. A recent United Press International news story reported that a fifteen-year-old had written an article for her high school paper on birth control. This is a newsworthy item? For whom? For parents? That's the breed of folks who often won't look at what's happening. This girl was almost expelled from school because of her essay. So many adults are living in an imaginary world.

CHAPTER SEVEN

Suicide

"Doctor, I've just taken twenty seconals. Will I die?"

It was a late night phone call as are most suicide calls. Night seems to multiply feelings of loneliness and desperation. Her voice had not reached the drug-soaked slurring stage, so I suspected that she had not taken the capsules but was calling for information and help.

"It's a big dose," I said cautiously, not answering her question in order to provide a little time for us both to get to the real problem.

"I haven't menstruated in two months, and I know I'm pregnant. I'd rather die than have a baby! I'm in school. I don't have any money, and my father is out of work," she added breathlessly.

"How old are you?" I asked, trying the stall technique.

She didn't even hear me. What did age matter anyway?

"I haven't any money for an abortion or anything. I just want to die—now, tonight!"

"Have you really already taken those pills?" I asked.

"No, but they are here in my purse. I got them from this man who comes around the school selling drugs."

I sighed with relief as I put down my little black book containing the phone numbers for Crises Centers.

"The fact that you've missed two months doesn't mean that you're pregnant," I said firmly.

"But you don't understand. I'm dizzy and vomit all the time." She began to cry.

"Come by my office tomorrow. We'll talk it over, and it won't cost you a thing. A day more or less won't matter," I stated, and then added heartlessly. "Besides, don't think suicide will help your family financially. Funerals cost money, too." I hoped to shock her into reality.

She sighed, thanked me, and hung up.

I had forgotten to ask her name and telephone number. A doctor never grows accustomed to these calls, but they are not as rare as a layman might think. It takes time to gear the mind for a crisis, and after such a call, you are always plagued with a nightmare of things you should have said.

The young girl came to the office the next day, and her pregnancy test was negative. It was an old, old story.

Test for Pregnancy

Many females think they are pregnant when they are not. This is caused by the fact that they have been exposed to a chance of pregnancy, or may have a sudden irregularity in their menstrual periods. "I've always been regular as clockwork," the worried patient says. The answer is often two answers. (1) She didn't actually keep a written record of her periods, but had a female subconscious guess. (2) Projection of periods was wrong. Many girls who think they are regular are surprised when they write down the exact date a period starts and ceases. This record, kept over a twelve-month period, will show variation from 22 to 35 days. Often this indicates a mild hormonal imbalance, but it is nothing to worry about.

The most certain sign of early pregnancy is the positive pregnancy test. The symptoms of nausea, vomiting, frequency of urination, soreness of breasts, etc., can be coincidences. They can, in part, be stimulated by a worried mind.

The positive test for pregnancy can often be gotten before you skip your second period. If there is any doubt as to the accuracy of the test, your doctor will tell you why, and when to return for a repeat examination. Incidentally, there is no shot or pill that your doctor can give you to "start a period" if you are pregnant. An abortion, either induced or spontaneous, is the only way the products of conception are expelled.

I include this statement because in the practice of gynecology we have many patients who have missed periods. Basically, this does them no harm if they are not trying to get pregnant, but psychologically, they receive much mental trauma. They equate menstrual bleeding with the same process as emptying the bladder. They think this is a poison that must be excreted from their bodies to allow normal female functioning to take place. This is ridiculous and is further reinforced by their telling a friend or an older person that they skipped a period last month. The answer from their female advisor is, "You did!" This implies everything from cancer to a total lack of femininity. This stimulus, added to your own doubts about your pregnancy status, builds up to be a tremendous mental hurricane. Only, unlike a hurricane, it doesn't pass off in a few hours. To appease the storm, we doctors often prescribe oral hormones that will bring on a normal period IF the patient isn't pregnant. It doesn't always cause menstruation but usually does.

Where to Get a Pregnancy Test

One gets a pregnancy test at several places: a doctor's office, a public health clinic, a Planned Parenthood clinic, a Birthright office, and other places depending upon the locale of the community. In the larger urban areas, the above places are present. In the more rural populations, your doctor's office is the place. If you think you have an unwanted pregnancy and are embarrased to go to your family doctor, throw such a feeling out the window. All doctors are aware of this problem just as much as all doctors are aware of the doctor-patient confidential relationship. In my experience, I have NEVER heard a second hand story of some doctor telling a young girl's parents that she came by for a test, and she was found to be pregnant. This kind of information is held in the strictest security files of professional ethics. In the rural areas, your doctor may be the only person who can guide you to a counselor if you are pregnant. I didn't say an abortionist; I said, *a counselor*. As this chapter develops, you will easily see the difference.

If the test is positive, confirming pregnancy, there is usually instant panic, tears, anger, depression, and doubt. This is normal in all age groups. Any or all of these emotions may be present. If the pregnancy is definitely unwanted, the next questions are: "What do I do now?" and, "Where do I go?"

Answering this last question is possibly the most serious part of this book. The unwanted pregnancy seems to demand an instant solution. That is, where can I go to get "it" out? Where can I get an abortion? Any quick answers to these questions are wrong. A stalling answer which is insincere is just as wrong. The female, talking to a counselor, doctor, minister, or agency, will usually have in the back of her mind two assumptions. (1) He (or she) just doesn't understand. (2) She has never been faced with this problem. True, I didn't use "he" in this sentence, but I do know of hundreds of patients who have received excellent counseling from "he's." If any advisor tells you to get an abortion now, you should look elsewhere for advice. On the other hand, if the advisor starts off with the statement that if you have an abortion, it's murder, you should just as quickly get another person who is professionally trained to advise you. These two extremes are often in the abortion clinics and too frequently in some religions. You should get opinions and more opinions. Contact Planned Parenthood Clinics, although they often stress abortion too much. Birthright Organizations and Abortion Crisis Centers are helpful. Check the yellow pages. Remember, you are about to make a decision that definitely will affect your life. It's more important than most other decisions you will ever make.

Be careful. Some abortion clinics are unethical. They have been known to give patients a positive pregnancy test when the woman was not pregnant. (As reported by the United Press International in July, 1974.)

A Protestant minister called me on the phone and requested that I do an abortion on his eighteen-year-old daughter. He didn't think, or know, of the mental and physical factors involved—both immediate and delayed —that might present themselves. When I gave him an appointment to bring his daughter by for a conference the next day (early), he hung up. This man was desperate. If the patient or her family get the "do it now" attitude, all will live to regret it. Why didn't this man take time to come by and talk the problem over eyeball to eyeball? In spite of his theology, his love for his daughter's well-being was the most important factor. At least, that was his thinking at that moment. I stressed to him that she should have options. But he flatly refused. He finally phoned one of my colleagues, had the abortion done, and now his daughter is in the hands of a psychotherapist. If there had been counseling, I know this wouldn't have been the end result. This case is explained to stress and restress the damage done by making a hasty judgment. Medically, the week's difference doesn't make one bit of difference. It can make all the difference in the person's life. An abortion isn't something that has to be handled like a severed artery or an acute appendix. The fast way out of the problem always seems the best, but if that way offers

to their sermons, but on a one-to-one basis, they are usually very experienced in advice and guidance. They can be of tremendous help with your family, too.

Eighteen to Twenty Plus Age Group

Your parents come in here as in the younger age group. The difference for you is that the Supreme Court has declared you an adult. Go to a doctor as early as possible. Get the tests. You have more options. Marriage is one of them, but whatever option you choose, get your diagnosis early, and then you will have much more time (a week at least) to evaluate the choices as how to handle your situation. Your girlfriends will often sympathetically lead you to a production line abortion clinic. Don't, and DON'T. Get the counseling that is available from altruistically trained people. The help may be from your doctor, your minister, your counselor, or a recognized social agency. Doctors and psychiatrists often have a too-busy schedule to give immediate appointments. Even reliable agencies may have counselors who give you no choice but an abortion. Many social workers are very liberal due to lack of experience or excess of hardship cases. You should have an unbiased opinion on each choice presented you.

Incidentally, (but note well!), not one can tell you *what* to do. If one tries, get further help. This is very important. A didactic answer to all cases is again not thinking of you as an individual. It is just solving your problem for the time being. The personal understanding offered when you first consult them about your problem is completely shut off as soon as you have the abortion, if that is your choice.

The Married Woman Desiring an Abortion

This patient often has other children. Ninety-nine percent of unplanned pregnancies mean shock and depression for the mother. This is normal. Unless she is psychotic, she would give her life for one of her other children. She needs to be reminded that this unborn foetus already resembles one of her present progeny. It is a serious thought. The fact that her husband left her, or that they are in financial strains, or whatever, are not valid excuses for such dramatic action which may have delayed physical and mental bad results.

Abortions for frivolous reasons are emotionally dreadful. It is academic to discuss whether or not it is murder. The simple fact is that you either create a baby or kill it. Should no one have an abortion? Of course some should, but the motive should be carefully weighed. Counseling is urgently advised. Write down your questions. If the counselor says, "There is nothing to it, you'll walk out a new person," don't believe him. Abortion is not like appendicitis. There can be enormous emotional and physical consequences. The young do not seem to suffer as much from this as those in the more mature bracket.

This is not to minimize the hardship cases. Abject poverty presents another situation as do other special problems. I recently advised the abortion procedure for a patient who had two children with IQs of less than 60.

This patient was delivered of a normal baby and sterilized by tubal ligation. A year later she became pregnant. Four percent do. She was aborted because a genetic study indicated a 95% chance for the pregnancy to have the inherited mental retardation.

The complications of having an early abortion are as follows:

1. **Infection—fairly rare.**
2. **Hemorrhage—fairly rare.**
3. **Sterility—not as rare as first thought.**
4. **Depression—usually not too bad.**
5. **Delayed depression—(One to five years). This is more often experienced when a planned baby is birthed, and the "mother instinct" takes over. The patient realizes she has aborted a foetus that may be like her present baby. This can take some drastic forms, and psychiatric therapy is often needed.**

CHAPTER EIGHT

Our Children

Ms. Williams was fifty-five years old, attractive, but tense. "I've never fainted before in my life, and it scared me," she said. "I'm just so tired all the time. I'm still working, of course. The children can spend the money faster than I can make it."

Ms. Williams was a widow and a successful real estate agent. A physical examination had shown no particular medical problems. She appeared to be in a concerned state of nerves. "I'm wiped out tired," she complained again, "and I'm so afraid I'll faint again."

"Think back. Did you stand up too fast"? I asked, dodging the low blood sugar angle that I often pull out because it's patient satisfying. I thought her problem was mostly tension, but she was not mentally ready for me to spell it out.

"No," she said uncertainly. "I had just had a call from

my daughter. She has disappointed me so many times. This time she wanted more money for an abortion. Abortion! She didn't even ask me; she just told me. I don't believe in abortion, but what's the alternative? I certainly can't support her marriage."

She sighed and added, "Whatever is wrong with the young people anyway? Betty is really a good girl. She has so much going for her. The young just can't seem to get it all into one ball of wax these days."

"It's tough out there on the college campus," I said lamely, feeling sorry for both mother and daughter.

Ms. Williams had been a patient for a long time. After the sudden death of her husband, I had seen her progress and discard tranquilizers and finally mature to the point of accepting her responsibilities. She was sharp and attractive in every way. Daughter Betty was outstanding, too. She was a cheerleader, as well as the class president, the kind of daughter who is a delight in high school. Yet now in college, she was reducing Mother to a bundle of nerves.

It is tough out there on the multiple choice campus. Beautiful, idealistic girls and boys with excited eyes are looking for life. Real life. But they have many choices that home, school, and church haven't logically explained. Reality is often all hormone choices—and in what direction do you point enthusiasm?

Professors may arrogantly say that there is no god, so students throw out all those silly myths. And so now what? It's a whole new world of free thinking. The required courses of freshman math, science, and English often discard the old thought patterns of Faith, but they don't spell out the new morals or ethics. They are often there, but they are drowned in too deep water. At seventeen, you don't have the trained ear or the sophisticated mental apparatus to hear. Besides, who has the time? There are boys, music, and campus games. The world is at spring. Who wants to battle anything? It's exploration time! Life is great!

And too often the exuberant Bettys come to the point of sex and abortion. And then what? What is the choice of the sophisticated college student?

Most young people, though, are not aware of how far they have come in recent years. Let's look at a little past history.

Do You Know About the "Baby Farms?"

One hundred years ago, in lieu of mass abortions, there were "baby farms," primarily for illegitimate children. These prospered in England as late as 1879. The "farms" accepted babies for a lump sum. The sooner the infant died, the more money for the "farmer." There was not much chance for survival, and the infant suffering was wholesale. The religious attitude in our country saved America from such merciless slaughter of illegitimates, but still children survived only by way of a cruel, sinful road perpetrated by man. Foetal slaughter does not reach this proportion of insensitivity, but it is certainly on the historical slate for question.

Before modern times, parents hired out their children. Children were a financial asset in supporting the family. Six and seven year olds were often chained to the machinery, working as long as sixteen hours a day. Factory owners were happy with the arrangement because they did not have to pay high wages. The children were too young to organize labor troubles. Their small hands were an advantage in manipulating machines. Many children died after a few years of this work, but fathers easily arranged for mothers to procreate more, so there was usually another to take the dead child's place. It was not until 1833, in England, that the first successful child labor law was enacted. In this country, Massachusetts, in 1836, was the first state to provide a similar law.

In the Middle Ages, it was estimated that only every other child lived to the age of ten. In the early 1900s, twenty to twenty-five percent of babies died. It is one of the major victories of medicine, education, and love that the figure has been reduced to under two percent.

In the early 1900s, America settled into a great child welfare movement. The American Association for the Study and Prevention of Infant Mortality, the Federal Children's Bureau, the American Child Health Association, and other organizations were originated. The concept was that every baby had a right to the best possible conditions and social climate. The medical specialty of pediatrics originated in America. It included not only the care of babies but care of older children in their mental as well as physical development. Obstetrics as a specialty was evolved because the good health of the mother was recognized as of great importance to the baby's development, even before birth. As we know, the growth changes are much more rapid in the prenatal state than after birth. Programs were set up which provided prenatal clinics to educate the mother concerning conditions that would harm the foetus. Carefully supervised diets were developed. Vitamin supplements were advocated. This trend developed healthy, happy babies —born under the supervision of an obstetrician and passed on to the care of pediatricians.

The Cult of Youth

So the baby grew healthily to youth. Today, we have the Cult of Youth. And what is "Youth" doing? He shouts about "doing his own thing" as if it were some sort of great new religion.

But what is he really doing beyond listening to his hair grow?

He complains that life is uncertain. So what? Life has always been uncertain. Pick an era and take a look. The handiest one is the parents' generation because the parents show the scars they have acquired. The average run-of-the-mill parents aren't running a pornography shop, supplying drugs, or operating topless, bottomless bars. They are trapped in a generation that has been filled with war, youth demands, and taxes to support the elderly. They may have believed in the concepts of discipline, but they have followed the permissive, submissive rule of child behavior promoted by the authoritative voices of the time. Intimidated by child psychology books that said, "Don't suppress your child's ego," they flattened their own ego. They were told that their child should be as free from problems as possible. They were indoctrinated with the concept that intelligent, empathizing parents could rear a nearly perfect generation of children. The phrase "love withdrawal" was used as a whip. No matter how difficult your child, you must make him feel secure. The broad base of love operated upon a value of permissiveness in order to avoid child frustration as opposed to the value of discipline. Granted that for lazy parents permissiveness is often more pleasant and effortless than wise and fair discipline, but the Bible says that love should be tempered with wise discipline. The nature of man is to take what he can get and to want more. Our children went from tricycles to bicycles, motorcycles, and cars. Each time there was more independence but less of the enforced disciplines of time and speed. They missed the all-important matter of maturity. The tricycle required little maturity. But as the wheels grew bigger and more powerful, trouble set in. Parents pressed and hoped for more communication. Children turned from the constant "why" and "tell me" to their own version that "silence is golden" and "what mother doesn't know won't hurt her." But the silence did hurt. Youth seemed to lack responsibility, respect, and love for family. Youth had arrived at the current age of 15 to 18 (post-puberty but short of maturity) by way of love, sacrifice, protection, and immunization shots. So it was their time to give a little, too. But they didn't.

Youth responded to over-protection and abundance of "things" by "who am I" and "hate the establishment." Again, the parents tried to understand, but it was next to impossible. They had been reared in the age of wars, job scarcity, and future uncertainties. Hadn't everyone? Historically the young had always coped constructively with the age at hand. The eras of the early settlers, the Revolution of 1776, as well as of the Civil War, had more difficult problems without the security of medical care, welfare, drug centers, rap houses, and counseling. Our youth balked and played games in an ineffectual effort to blueprint the Boston Tea Party, but they reversed the slogan from "taxation without representation" to "representation without taxation." In spite of the clatter, parents continued to sacrifice for their children by supporting married teenagers through college, supplying money for abortions, adopting their offspring, often illegitimate, and financing for lawyers for youth's drug involvement. Regardless of age, any fair-minded person can see the tragedy.

Parents run mad and scared. They love their children, and they still want the best for them. But nothing will make them agree that polygamy, polyandry, drugs, and communes are the "Good Life." It is back to the primitive within the security of welfare from family or government that youth seems to want. But who is to provide the welfare? In the meantime, what's happened to communication? Communication is giving and receiving, but with our young, it seems to be changed to disagreement. There is no compromise in the "I'm right and you're wrong" argument. The "you just don't understand" phrase is just as conflicting.

The ivory towers were torn down by the confrontations of the 60s. We are beginning to get more realism from this segment of influence. It was all right when the children told their parents what to do, but it wasn't so A-OK when they told the halls of learning what to do. The products of permissiveness didn't harden into ambition, determination, and respect for the formulas of history and culture. They demanded representation on the governing board. "Representation? Why they had no experience!" the schools said. "No knowledge, no wisdom!" the professors said. These were the things that Mother knew when she said, "come home early" to her children with over-functioning id's. It was the same id that had been so carefully nurtured by parents who read and listened to the voices of psychologists. Educators saw selfishness, insensitivity, a lack of intellectual curiosity, and a strong sense of self-fulfillment. Perhaps the basis of love, work, and ambition may not be inherited, but instilled. Watching today's youth is as nerve severing as watching trapeze artists without a net. And what a circus youth has created with mindless clowns and dirty sawdust! And this is certainly a frivolous way to express it. They kill themselves by rotten choices and kill the grandchildren by abortion. They make an orgy of being bored in a world of sex, pot and shots of cocaine.

Youth, you've come a long way up the road to survival, all the way from asset to liability. History grins like a crocodile as it belches up the bloody facts of a hundred-odd years ago. When you consider that there are many living people today who are over a hundred years old, the time lag quickly collapses. What a long way you've come! All the way from field to factory to education and leisure. In primitive times, the family picked beans together. Then came the factory; it was a whole new scene.

And where are we? I believe the children who aren't lost in the pile will pull themselves together into adults.

There were true values in the ideal of the id. They will look, listen, and grow through belated hardships. Their children will be different. Perhaps the parents' thinking, with the help of child guidance, will meet discipline again with faith in God or ethics, and the grandchildren will be a joy. Perhaps they will know that in a world of risks there is no guarantee of personal security. Certainly all young people have not gone the way of drugs and sex, but it is the biggest parent scare. As youths realize the moon is not made of cheese, they will cooperate. Discontent has long been regarded as the mother of invention. Love oils the wheels—love for one's self, one's partner, and one's children. It should fan out in love for neighbors, society, and the world. This love buds and flowers first in the home. Tomorrow's families will be armed with a freedom that they never had before, but perhaps they will look on it as the great treasure that it is. Assuming that this generation will have the good sense to know that marriage is the necessary base for a family, they are off to a good start. With better educated mothers as well as fathers, women liberated from the concept of cooks, maids, and second-class citizens, we can have a balanced family based on mutual love, understanding, and discipline.

Desperation moved us into the direction of sex education, and it's reward will be in the area of the family, but that education must begin early. The high school level will generally reach the middle class, but there are too many school drop-outs to risk the chance of waiting. This should be started on a much younger level. The father-mother, man-woman, child-parent relationships deserve the best of care. This is the peace that the sex revolution and war between the sexes promises. The child-parent tragedy of the sixties and the seventies can never be justified, but experience and study can result in relevance.

America has always wrapped its body and mind in the flags of education and conscience. Today, as never before, we have young people with sincere causes seeking this direction. More and more concerned young people want to be in the exciting field of education in order to better pattern their lives. Hoorah! This is the challenge of our times. Science has produced materialism, and creature comforts are great. Medicine gives good health, and it is a blessing. The equally large and encompassing field of education will provide the means to enjoy both.

It seems to me that this generation cut the chains from both women and children. Although the results, such as sex, freedom, and abortion have been traumatic to moral values, good can evolve. It takes time to adjust to a change in society. Perhaps we will have a new hybrid flower, only more flamboyantly colorful with greener leaves and a stronger stem. The youth of today understand the challenge. Who knows? Perhaps they will be the proud nurturers of the Blue Ribbon hybrid species.

But, as concerns abortion, youth has been thrust into the role of a mature adult while still at the mercy of the strong hormonal drives of a young body. And it has happened at a time in history when the young are least prepared to accept responsibility.

Youth, are you really ready to make the decisions involved? Is it not true that you will most likely tend to use abortion as birth control? Won't you find the "Trojan Horse" expedient—and be unaware of dangers it contains?

I raise the questions, because, as a physician, my own attitude toward abortion has developed across the years out of contact with the realities of the situation.

Will you be an asset to society in the matter—on a plane far transcending the asset you were when you were exploited? Or, will you, yourself, exploit abortion, becoming one of society's tragic liabilities?

We hesitate to put on paper the second assumption of this book lest we alienate the young readers whom we love. But, if honesty really is the best policy:

Legal abortion puts into the hands of American youth a power they will not use wisely—at first.

The Role of Youth

In most instances, abortion judgments will be made by youthful women. More babies are created by the potency of the sex drive in the vigor of youth. But youthful mothers are more likely than older ones to be uninformed. Health agencies and similar organizations are making good and adequate information available in the underprivileged and uneducated areas of the country. Sex education in the schools will also act as a preventative of pregnancy. Crusaders for these and other similar measures are not trying to undermine the morals of the country. They have taken a look at the misery of women, babies, and children and are trying to do something to prevent this agonizing situation. Certainly, sex education without

morals is animalistic. But the younger generation has
declared war on the old morality. The youth cry, "Hypocrites!" Perhaps the young are right. They see horror and
great suffering. They see desperate cries for help. They
want practical solutions, not moral preachments. A moral
society often plays games and doesn't see or hear. The
heathen and the saint are forever in battle—and the
saint doesn't make it to all the parties! In the meantime,
the problems of women and children increase. The truth
is that many women are exploited, and that poverty and
misery are like snakes, coiled and striking. The problems
are not limited to the ghettos.

People may be too small for the God of the Bible, but
often both the heathen and the saint are trying. Lip
service to faith never won a halo, and hypocrisy never
had less breathing space than now. Confronted with
legal abortion, the opinionated and the old, the gloomy
Joe's and the horrified Hattie's, will carp and predict
zero population and no morality, but the young will be
challenged, and the young in mind will offer wisdom.
Women are women. I believe that in greater freedom
they will find a better and more honest way to build this
world. They will be the same stalwarts of civilization that
they have always been.

Will Legal Abortion be Used Wisely?

Philosophically speaking, what is abortion? Freedom
for women? A better world? Or, "Murder, Incorporated"?
All proponents of the abortion legislation believe the
former; many sincere Christians believe the latter. As

each sees it, both teams are trying for the salvation of the individual and the world, but the two will never get together. Does it matter? Since abortion is legal, Woman can make the choice. Yet when this new freedom rests on the shoulders of the very young, the answer may revert back to the family—and the mother especially. Will the freedom be used with responsibility?

And so regardless of age, you must evaluate and live in this point of time. You can condemn with frozen minds, or you can choose a wider path and offer help. In the midst of wild male predictions, the path will be found.

CHAPTER NINE

Mother Can Have an Abortion, Too

"I just know I'm pregnant again," Mrs. Dobson spoke breathlessly. "I haven't menstruated in six weeks, and I have all the symptoms. My husband is going to Japan on business next month, and I plan to go with him. And now this!"

The pregnancy test had been negative, but in the earlier stages, the test may not be accurate. There was a good chance that she was pregnant. "I'll give you a prescription that will start your period if you aren't pregnant. If it doesn't, come back in two weeks. We'll run another test. They are more accurate in eight weeks."

"Well, of course I won't have another baby," she stated positively. "Forty years old is too old. We have had our family."

I didn't believe what I was hearing. I had birthed all three of Gloria Dobson's beautiful children. She was a good mother and a sensible, healthy woman with no economic problems. There are days when the ob-gyn doctor feels as though no one in the whole wide world wants a baby except the hopelessly sterile patient. Whatever has happened to the feeling that "you hold the whole world in your hands when you hold a baby." Was the old song worn out? Didn't women ever hear it anymore?

Mrs. Dobson came back in four weeks, and her test was positive. "Yes, I'm going to have the baby," she sighed as if suffering the last stages of terminal illness.

Unplanned pregnancies always seem to be a depressing shock. Mothers appear to remember all work and no joy. And yet later, as grandmothers, they exude quick love and eager enthusiasm. What is it? Are the thirty-five and forty year olds tired of human horticulture and ready to kill a baby for a trip to Japan? In an age when women struggle to maintain youth by way of outward appearance, do they forget that children keep them young by shifting them from one thought generation to another? Are they so eager to start developing their own personal life style that they don't realize personality development is a steady process of OUR TEAM instead of ME? Unless you are a firm speaker in platitudes, this subject can leave you hanging by the thumbnails.

What of the Child?

And what of the hated little hitchhiker in the womb? It's not his fault he's there. The knowledge that there is no one else like him in the world will not be of comfort when his cradle has all the warmth of a grave.

It was once rumored that emotions effect the foetus. I hope not. The waves of hatred toward him would dim those shining, excited eyes before he was born. And what of the love and trust that his small heart will be so ready to give?

Before mothers start to abort their unplanned pregnancies, a little philosophizing won't hurt them. Times are different for Mother, too. She no longer stitches "Home Sweet Home" plaques in her spare time. She has more creative hobbies. Modern woman's life promises careers, committees for causes, sports, parties, and mental pursuits. In her world of many choices, babies and children can be a handicap. The Trojan Horse has raced to suburbia. And here is another place that the right of abortion can be abused. The chance is there, but like Mrs. Dobson and our young, she will stop for time to think. Psychologists say that humans don't have instincts for mother love. They have drives and motivations. But whatever they are called, they are not hanging on hooks in cold storage. They are as old as Woman, but not expired. It is my experience that women stick by their basic principles no matter what.

And so you're pregnant with a baby rejection. How can a male obstetrician possibly relate to all your problems? It's not very hard. My wife and I had child rejection, too. Our babies were planned, but we clearly recognized the fact that children make for brat-type troubles, clamor, interruptions and inconvenience. We enjoyed the peace of our two-together world, and we suspected that there were lessons to be learned in discipline and self-centered pleasures. Had we known how truly character polishing for us our children would be, we would have been even more hesitant in accepting the parent role. But I share the miracle of creation with each patient, and watch the second miracle of instant love for the newborn. And I identify. I will never forget the day the hospital nurse pulled back the nursery curtains and there was a black haired, wide-eyed, eight pound beautiful baby with a pink bow in her hair—not born with this bow, even though I thought my status as a fledgling doctor could even accomplish this feat.

My personal experience with patients after nine months always retells the same story. It's pure corn, but it's also pure fact. Sophistication has not strained out the primitive drive. I cracked up internally when I saw my own newborn baby, and in a feminine fashion, my wife's reaction was the same as mine. The love in her eyes was much better than a soap opera actress striving for bigger and better roles. After discharge from the hospital, we tiptoed into the room to see if the sleeping baby was still breathing; if she cried, we picked her up in ten seconds. We did everything the pediatrician said not to do by way of spoiling the baby. It is not my purpose to yes or no the abortion question. There are many valid reasons for the choice of abortion, but in suburbia, the budget can stretch, though often not without sacrifice; at thirty-five or forty years old, you can afford to wait a few more years for your trip to Japan.

CHAPTER TEN

Sex, Education, Revolution, and War

Education, biology and experience are factors that will deal with the challenges of the amazing confrontations of the young. The not-so-young have the same problems, but they are aging downhill and are not as much cause for concern.

If this generation of parents can stop sobbing and get on with the business at hand, the whole picture can constructively change. Sex education is necessary. We do not have an unexpected moral explosion; it has been spawning and hatching for a long time. It is not the young group that conceives and publishes pornography, writes and produces literature, shows the movies, deals the drugs to the pushers, and legalizes abortion. It is the adult world. The young are the inheritors not the instigators. We cannot escape, and we cannot go back. Who wants Victorian days anyway? It was the golden age of hypocrisy.

Many objectors to sex education have not given in-depth thought to the situation. It is not a "how to" subject taught like mathematics, but a panorama involving morals, social behavior, family life, birth control, parenthood and child rearing, along with boy-girl relationships —growth, venereal disease and mating. These subjects should not be isolated into a single course, but should be enmeshed in the curriculum of social sciences, hygiene, home economics, and biology. Teachers and parents need to comprehend the overall structure of the program and the realistic thinking behind it.

Parents have tended to fight for sex quarantine too long. Seminars are needed for parents, too. Legalized abortion has intensified the issue. We love our young, and it is imperative that we equip them with the knowledge to handle their lives.

It is easy for parents of faith to point the way of the Bible because certainly the Bible is clear on every facet of sex thinking, but unfortunately, we cannot religiously isolate our young people. Youths are bold and often blown by the wind. It might help, however, if churches could speak more directly to sex issues.

Sex education is a prophylactic and teaches a great deal. A lack of education causes many pathetic casualties. Reason and practicality will win. As in every revolution, there is tragedy, but there are also gains in knowledge and wisdom. Good will certainly come from our experimentation, but all revolutions reach a plateau in vision. Bloody slaughter of babies by abortion will be replaced by responsibility and insight such as we have never had before. Boys will learn as much as girls about the depth of responsibiltiy, and maybe their age-old happy swinging "Who? me?" attitude can be more realistically channeled into values that will give personalized male insight. The necessity for sex education is a real gain in the family study, and the now and future years will profit. Wisdom and insight are never easy and never without examples of casualties. This period of change is rough on seasoned parents, but is even worse on the young. They are idealistic and inexperienced in the thing called living.

The Need for Monogamy

In the world of biology, most creatures are monogamous until their young are independent. It is a nightmare to think that the human female will be less than the animal. Reason civilized her. She will not long be exploited or enslaved by the so-called "New Morals," and she will not give up the family concept, in spite of the glamorous propaganda of communes, pads, open dormitories, trial marriages, promiscuity, and fun on the water bed. Nor will she continue to wander around looking for a "sex fix." The family as an institution for the human race is just as valid and necessary as it is for the lower animals. Even if moral values bore you, it is impossible to ignore this lesson from the animal world. "Equality of sex" is a simple phrase and should be legally accepted, but law and freedom never say that there is a reproductive equality of the sexes. The ability to reproduce has a built-in restriction with penalties and a sense of responsibility peculiar to women. This must assert itself. It is the difference between male and female. Sex philosophers often tend to ignore or underestimate the power inherent in reproductive organs. In animals, the choice is restricted, but humans can reason. Animals are sex guided by force of nature that periodically calls for mating seasons. It is a demand. Humans have a choice, but forces of nature still beckon around the mating corners, demanding motherhood and family. Sex is inherently more than emotional communications.

Every man has always had the dream of a free sexual society. For him, this is happy hunting time in Lotus Land, but women will eventually draw the rules. In the sex dance, somebody must. How cunning of men to devise the "sex is fun" and "how can anything so beautiful be wrong?" and "chastity is a bore" phrases. Their sex drives appear so virile. Eve first tempted Adam, and he ate the whole apple. But is Adam ever getting even? Men have built a new trap for women, and it says that chastity is no virtue. But girls will eventually take up the slogan that they dropped. Chastity outside of marriage IS a virtue if for no other reason that it's practical and to the female's advantage. She will not be outsmarted by men. The doomsday holy Joe's are wrong, because women are not fools. It may take years of experimentation with free love to arrive at this point, but even this is doubtful. It is rare that I see the satisfied, happy, unmarried common-law wife in the office, whether pregnant or not. Sex can never be as much fun for women as for men. Those reproductive organs and hormones are devious and tricky factors to consider. The young female glandular dilemma cannot be cured by a concentrated shot of male flattery. She has her problems with the pill. She has cystitis, and painful menstruation, along with an occasional case of venereal disease. The joy of sex love is too brief compared to the built-in complications of ovaries, uterus, and an unwanted pregnancy. There is no equality in this.

The sex revolution came first, but all-out sex war will follow as Eve realizes that Adam is trying to give back that apple. And so we are now having a strange new philosophy for women. But how long do you think they will be so innocently naive? The ultimatum that men make the sex experience as desirable for their partner as for themselves is a great advancement. And that is the equality and value that will stand. The pendulum will certainly swing conservatively back, but not without new sensitivity and beauty.

The Pendulum of History

A pendulum is a body hung from a fixed point so that it can swing hypnotically to and fro under the forces of gravity and momentum. Historically, the gravity of a situation and momentum of change moves civilization. It swings relentlessly from war to peace, from restricted to submissive, from slavery to freedom, from conservative to liberal. This historical pendulum gains luster and polish from its forward thrust, so it's really never again the same. Women will go back to the conservative for no other reason at all except self-preservation. But their

attitudes have been recycled, and they will have profited
by new freedom and new evaluations of sex and family.
Men will have learned that they can't subjugate women
as in the past, and the family is important. But above all,
they will know that two swinging freely side by side is
better than two walking Indian file.

The wisdom gained from this generation is trial and
error, and this is precious. But never think that it hasn't
had its female martyrs. They won't make the cover of
Time magazine; in fact, they may not even make it in the
smallest unit of family life, and that is tragic. They may
never experience the kind of love that only the trials of
marriage can build. Women have always been aware
of the altar of sacrifice for family, and usually it has been
worth it. The fun sex altar is not worth the sacrifice of
abortions and emotional strain. Females have over-
reacted to sex and given men a real ego trip. The free
swinging male with his eternal "Who, me?" attitude
doesn't deserve the best of female thoughtfulness, tenderness, or love. He is not lovable like a child, and he does
not love with childlike faith and trust. Women will walk
away from men with their ridiculous uncomfortable pads,
charmless motels, uncomfortable back seats, and damp
sandy blankets by the sea. A woman's sex can create a
beautiful home with all that the word implies, and anything less is degrading and exploitive. This age experi-
ments, but it will learn and pass on its deep-found
wisdom and strength to the next generation. The bright-
eyed, happy girls will not be sex liberated victims. They
will be free, but not tricked by definitions and promises
of careless fun relationships. When women realize that

sex is not dancing all the way, they will change the rules. Sex is also selectivity, and the selection may no longer be man's choice, but woman's choice. Perhaps this is as it should be. After all, it is they who have control of the reproductive organs.

The luster of the new pendulum will certainly include the right of choice without social condemnation and a world of smirking males. The female who wishes to swing the arc away from the majority will be free to do so. Just as each is created differently, so each has free choice.

Part Three: Morals

A look at ultimate authority.

CHAPTER ELEVEN

Is Abortion Murder?

Karen Butler was thirty-five years old and honest. She was attractive, intelligent, not married, and pregnant.

"Doctor I'm divorced with two teenage daughters. I had planned to marry this week, but my fiance was killed in an accident last month." She paused, but did not dissolve in tears. She was past tears. Life had already been too hard. "It's not as though I didn't use birth control," she continued, "I thought the IUD was adequate. Obviously it wasn't. I don't see how I can continue to support my girls and have a baby, too. I am alone; there's no one to help. Now I want your opinion. Is abortion murder?"

I fumbled around with a pencil, and she filled the silence with this statement. "I believe in God. I even believe in Jesus Christ. And while I'm on the subject, I

123

may as well say that I believe sex without marriage is sin. What do *you* think?"

My phone thankfully buzzed, and I was able to prolong the interruption. I needed time. More time than I could find. How do you get out of quicksand?

How much moral and religious counseling is required of an obstetrician?

As an obstetrician, should I have to wonder whether or not the foetus has a soul? Ensoulment is out of the medical department. All I know is that if I perform an abortion, a baby will not be born. The foetus was living, and now it is dead. If I see a featherless bird fall from the nest, flutter and die. I'm sorry. I'm even more sorry when it is a foetus. I like obstetrics. It is my life's work; I feel exhilarated every time I deliver a baby. They never cease to be miracles of creation and as such are precious. After many years of practice, this feeling doesn't diminish; it grows.

Is abortion murder? If it is, then the doctor is the murderer, and the pregnant one is only the accessory after the fact. The patient puts out a contract on the foetus, pays me, and I am the official killer. The guilt patients may later feel must be shared by me with person after person after person. This fact will bother some doctors, and others it will not, depending upon their thinking. If the patient gets the answer from the doctor, who will give the doctor his answer? The church? Yes, if the doctor has faith.

I will suggest that a patient go to her clergyman. It is the proper place for the discussion. If the patient doesn't want to go to a church or counselor, what do I say then? Religiously speaking, is abortion murder?

There is no "Thou shalt not abort" commandment in my medical book. The apparent needs of my patients determine my basic response. Doctors, whether they are religious or not, need to listen and prescribe. Tranquilizers for the patient do not always do the job, and they are habit forming and may produce lethargy and depression. Doctors may be forced to road test religious thoughts when considering whether or not they will abort a patient, because they need to treat the whole patient—body and mind.

Moses Would Recognize Us?

Would Moses be a good leader for the United States today? We are just as oversubscribed to sex and undersubscribed to morals as when he came down the mountain with those stone tablets. If he is still pointing to those things, how would he answer my patient's problem? Would he use his big temper and brilliant rhetoric to rack her back, or would he say Christ has a new way, and His understanding and sympathy will make a difference in the stone law? Christ didn't like the iffy type questions of the Pharisees, and He wouldn't be fond of this one either. The only conclusion that I can logically draw is that the Bible says the Lord doesn't change His mind, in which case I would have to say Moses is still holding those commandments as a guide.

Word has been blown about that many ministers campaigned for abortion so this gives religious approval to the subject. This is true of many dedicated clergymen but not the majority. I'm reminded of the old fable about the man who told a terrible lie concerning a friend. He went to a priest and confessed. The priest gave him a sack of feathers saying, "Put a feather on every doorway in the city." The man carefully did as he was instructed, reported back to say that the job was done. The priest praised him and said, "Now go back and pick them up again." The poor fellow went from door to door but the feathers had been blown all over the village, and he could not find a single one to put in his sack. The idea that abortion is moral has been blown around, and some of the young and also the more mature do not question it. If ministers starring in the abortion question have made a mistake, it will be very difficult to pick up those feathers.

Judging from the birth control issue, many doctors look to the churches for direction. The American Medical Association did not formally sanction medical birth control information until after the churches more or less zeroed in. In the Anglican church, the 1930 Lambeth Conference (Resolution fifteen) stated that, while abstinence was the primary and obvious method of limiting or preventing parenthood, other methods might be used. However, it strongly condemned contraceptive control for motives of selfishness, luxury, or mere convenience. Later the Episcopal Church stated that procreation of children was one but not necessarily the chief purpose of sex in marriage.

An obstetrician gives premarital sex facts to the brides-to-be just like the clergy only his facts are physical; spiritual facts are the department of ministers. We need a book by the church paralleling Dr. David Rubin's book, and we would call it "All the Spiritual Facts You Need to Know About Sex and Were Afraid to Ask." Church-going doctors would be the first to read and memorize it so that they could help pass the news along. If such a book had been written a few years ago, we might not have a sex revolution today. A ponderous, scholarly text will not fill the need. The need is for a small, practical handbook. Doctors have been busy writing the physical "How to Sex" manuals, but we cannot know the spiritual ground rules about *why* you feel that way unless the church cues us better. The Lord must surely have had His reason too.

What the Churches Say

What have the various churches said about abortion? Some of the clergy claim that abortion is freedom for women and a better world, while others call it Murder, Incorporated. Most advocates of abortion legislation call it the former, and most basic faith followers and Roman Catholics term it the latter. Both teams are trying for the salvation of the individual and the world. The two may never get together, but perhaps it really doesn't matter. Only the individual woman can make the choice for herself just as only the aborting doctor can decide for himself. Both doctor and minister meet on the common ground that sex and religion are two of the most potent forces of human drive that overthrow the power of reason. Abortion, the offspring of sexual motivation, is religious, moral, and personal to the marrow; the one involved needs objectivity and counseling. When the decision rests with the very young, the answer may revert back to the family and especially the mother. Father will usually supply the money. And so regardless of age, you may have to evaluate the subject. An examination of the various views may clarify the issue.

Since most Protestant churches have not been articulate, you don't hear much above the sound of shifting feet; some clergy believe one way and others another. They have become enmeshed in social action and hear the human cry of misery, poverty, and the population explosion. In England where the Anglican Church is the state church, a modified law allows abortion when pregnancy is harmful to the woman's life, her physical and mental health, her existing children, and in cases of hereditary disease. This law has been liberally interpreted and permissively administered; abortion mills are busy. The Church of England does not appear to have taken a strong stand on the issue. It seems the fashionable response is for abortion.

Moral outrage has been sounded about abortion by individual clergy members of various Liberal faiths, but no all-conclusive opinion has come or is likely to come. Frighteningly large abortion statistics and criticism may stir movement in these churches, for they believe in the basic concept of the Bible and Jesus Christ, but they don't buy the idea that every "jot and tittle" of the Bible is basic fact and truth. They believe love is permissively given, though of course not sexual love.

LOVE is the great big word that has to do with neighbors, race, brotherhood, in-laws, business competitors, and persons like this. Ends often justify means. For instance, if my patient goes to a minister, he may say that hers is a real hardship case which it most certainly is. "Yes, have an abortion," he may say. "God is just and loving; He knows and hears." This kind of love and justice is sponsored by the Bible more than somewhat frequently; it is preached just as often from the pulpits. Even a doctor can see that it is scriptural. Good ends, lovingly administered, can justify means. Aborting this particular foetus might give the good end of normalcy to the family; having the baby might shock and weaken the morals of the teenage daughters; the criticism and condemnation of their social world might have many cruel effects that would hurt them all their lives; and the money situation seems impossible.

This same clergyman may say, "Confess and repent the sin of unmarried sex. God is just and loving; He hears and He knows. If the abortion bothers you, pray about it." A just and loving God is certainly scriptural.

And what about the fundamentalists? Those who believe that every "jot and tittle" of the Bible is true? To them, the Bible is the Word of God, not a doctrine or a system of ethics. The Lord says what He means in His Holy Book, and it is to be read for content like any other book; it was inspired by God through the Holy Spirit.

In the belief that abortion is murder, fundamentalists point to numerous teachings of the Bible, but Psalm 139 says it rather succinctly, "You made all the delicate inner parts of my body and knit them together in my mother's womb. Thank you for making me so wonderfully complex! Your workmanship is marvelous—and how well I know. You were there while I was being formed in utter seclusion! You saw me before I was born and scheduled each day of my life before I began to breathe. Every day was recorded in Your book." (From *The Living Bible*.)

In less poetic words, the Bible is saying that God knows each life and has a plan for it from the mother's womb. So abortion is murder because the Bible says each life has a purpose in God's plan, and this is known to God when the foetus is in the womb. (I doubt that in this particular case the patient is a fundamentalist.) However, if she is, the minister will probably remind her that the Lord will provide for her as He does for all who look to Him and obey Him in faith. The Lord has promised this in His Book, and He is faithful to His promise. The fundamentalist concept builds a big protective wall and explains it. But often its members have judged many unmarried pregnant girls too harshly, forgetting the important love-forgiveness command. They reinforce a terminal righteousness and compose legalistic concept "thou-shalt-nots."

(Remember, I am not passing judgment on any particular religious group—fundamentalist, liberal, Catholic, or other. I am merely reporting the objective review of a physician.)

I have not had any Roman Catholic patients with the abortion question because it is not a question with them. The sex act is more than a commitment of two people; its creative, life-giving force leads to God and is holy.

In calling abortion murder, Catholics go back into the annals of church history. They have quite a lineage to go back to. They see that in Greek and Roman days abortion was a frequent occurrence. On the other hand, the Hebrew faith had a great respect for family, women, and individual life; Jews condemned abortion but found certain exceptions to it. The Christian message brought more importance to the individual and his life. The idea of an individual, animate immortal soul given by God to every human person and hopefully returning to Him for eternity was a powerful concept which, within two centuries, transformed the Roman Empire. The value of the born person became associated closely with a similar value granted to the unborn person, and as Christian beliefs crystalized in writing and tradition, condemnation of abortion came to be. (John Noonan, *The Morality of Abortion,* Harvard University Press, 1970.)

The Bible teaches specifically that Jesus was conceived in Mary's womb by the Holy Spirit. What grew in her womb from conception was not a blob of protoplasm, but the person of the God-man Jesus. Also clearly taught was that the infant John (the Baptist) "leaped" in the womb of Elisabeth. These specific references to the living personhood of the embryo were reinforced by the teachings of the Fathers of the Church. The Didache said, "You shall not slay the child by abortion." Clement of Alexandria condemned abortion, as did Athenagoras: "Those who use abortifacients are homicides." Tertullian said, "the mold in the womb may not be destroyed." The Council of Ancyra, in AD 314, denounced women who "slay what is generated." Another Council, in AD 305, at Alvira, excommunicated women committing abortion after adultery and would not even readmit them to the Church at the point of death. While Saint Jerome and Saint Augustine questioned when the rational soul was given by God, this did not affect their complete moral condemnation of abortion. In the late fourth century, Saint Basil wrote, "The hair-splitting difference between formed and unformed makes no difference to us. Whoever deliberately commits abortion is subject to the penalty for homicide." (The above from *Handbook on Abortion* by Dr. and Mrs. J. C. Wilkie, Hiltz Publishing Co., 1973.)

And so in the countdown each must make her own finite decision based on her own faith but not her convenience. And so we are right on the clock with the issues, but there are different strokes for different folks, and the same goes with the obstetrician and gynecologist, too. When we look at legalized abortion, there are many choices, and possibly our hypocrisy must fall. Women must assume the moral responsibility of the act. The decision may prove that we have to choose between faith as an absolute and faith as an abstraction.

CHAPTER TWELVE

Jesus People

Pixie was eighteen years of age and unmarried. She was dressed in blue jeans, and her long hair reached halfway down her back. She told me that she thought she was at least three months pregnant. Examination confirmed her diagnosis. As customary, I told her that I would talk with her in the conference room. Most of us in this specialty don't try to anticipate whether or not we'll be asked to do an abortion. Pixie's case was no different, but my follow-up dialogue with her was a surprise.

She told me that she wanted her baby. This was preceded by a short, factual account of why she was pregnant and her present attitude. She and her boyfriend had been on the drug scene. About two months back, she had been reached by some Jesus People. They had almost turned her off, but since they were her age, she had listened and now she was living at the Twenty-third

Psalm House. She told me frankly, happily, and positively that she had accepted Jesus Christ as her Saviour. She would definitely have her baby; she was trying to get her boyfriend to see what Jesus had done in her life so that he would be saved too. When I answered the question that the particular drug which she had taken prior to her conversion would not harm her unborn baby, she said, "Praise God and thank you Jesus."

Pixie had another last minute appointment with me late one afternoon. Everything about her was last minute, unplanned, unscheduled. Time was totally irrelevant; she hadn't noticed this and wouldn't have cared anyway. She was then six months pregnant and still living in the Jesus house. As I emptied my desk drawer of free sample vitamins for her, she praised the Lord for them, then suddenly stopped and leveled large, brown eyes at me.

"Doctor, are you saved? *Really* saved, I mean."

"Of course," I answered checking my watch. I was tired and wanted to go home. Besides I knew the answer to this one; I had had other Jesus people in my office. I added the magic phrase, "I believe Jesus Christ is my Lord and Saviour."

"Praise the Lord," she said happily then looked at me suspiciously, "Do you really know Him, I mean? You look awfully worried, just like my dad."

A daughter like Pixie was enough to make any dad look tired I thought, but from previous encounters with this new breed, I knew where the confrontation was headed. I hesitated; Pixie had never referred to her family before, and I had surmised she was a runaway from suburbia. Her parents had to be heartbroken; she was

a very special person in so many ways. Maybe a rec-
onciliation was possible, and I could help. "Where is
your home?" I asked casually, not wanting to pry.

"Miami," she stated not in the least deterred. "I'll
bet you fill all your spare time with trips, parties, and
things just like my folks. It's terribly empty, lonely too,
I'll bet, but people like that just don't even see it. They
think it's fun if you know what I mean."

"Not so," I said flatly, wondering if she would leave
if I stood up. She was gunning to give me that "You're
the establishment routine." My personal life and thoughts
were not her business, but her steady gaze warned me that
she was breaking out in Christian love and concern. But
wherever would she be if the Jesus people hadn't found
her? The thought slowed my irritation edge. The answer was clear—pregnant and probably lost on hard
drugs.

"Doctor, would you come down to the house with me
and meet some of the brothers and sisters?"

I guessed that she needed a ride back. "I'm in a hurry
to get home," I said, "but would you like a ride?" I
offered this a little grudgingly because it wasn't on my
way.

"Praise the Lord! I really need a ride. It was a long
walk over. Bill's outside, will you take him too?"

"Is he your boyfriend?" I asked.

Her laugh was infectious, "No, no, he couldn't see the
Jesus thing like me. Bill is my new boyfriend. We're
getting married next week. Isn't it just wonderful that
the Lord would send me somebody just about perfect like
Bill! He's who I've been looking for all my life. The

big love, you know what I mean. We are equally yoked, like the Bible says. It's just so exciting to watch the Lord work out all this for me and my baby. The Lord doesn't usually hurry so much, but He did this time. Christians need families for their babies."

She had learned a lot of Bible in a short time I thought. Bill, minus beard and long hair, would have figure-headed for the ideal establishment picture for the young man on the go. As it was, he was impressive and educated. His faded blue jeans and the Bible sticking out of his worn coat symbolized his life style.

An Attitude Toward Life

On the way to the Twenty-third Psalm House, their group-home, they talked. Their enthusiasm was so catching that my own tiredness lifted. They were in love with each other, the Lord, me, and all mankind, and they wanted to spread their wonderful joy and happiness to the whole world. I was the nearest likely convert, and they went to work fast.

Evidently deciding that I looked troubled, they told me it was a sin. "When you turn over your life to the Lord, He works it all out, you know," Pixie said. "You just trust the Lord—like me. Here I was pregnant and not married. And He sent me Bill."

"It's not always that easy," said Bill, who was an Elder at the house. "Mostly it's a long time before the Lord works out your problems. The point is that you have to trust. Trust—that's your peace, and your joy comes in praising His name. It's just that simple, you know. That's why we were born—to praise Him, you know, and to tell others about Him."

Even with all the "you knows" thrown in, I heard the message and was uncomfortable with the subject. "Before Bill came along did you ever think about an abortion?" I interrupted, being practical and also curious about how they planned to provide for the baby.

Pixie looked horrified. "Of course not!" but added more thoughtfully, "Maybe when I was doing the drug thing, I did. But not after I got with the Jesus group. It will all work out. Bill helps paint houses, and we put the money in the Psalm House bank account. That takes care of everybody's emergencies. When the money runs low, we all pray and fast and first thing you know the Lord sends us money—a check, somebody, or something."

I had already begun to wonder how much money I had in my wallet. I couldn't seem to hold conversation control so I interrupted again with, "What about your parents, do they know where you are?" I hoped to bring the discussion to my thoughts.

"No, but they will after the baby. They would just worry more," Pixie answered, but her voice seemed a little sad.

"I don't agree with her on that one," Bill said, and his love and concern for her was audible. "She loves them—it's just that she doesn't think they will understand. But we need to try. If they don't like us at first, maybe they'll think about it, and the next time we try, they will understand better. We are praying about it. The Lord will show us what to do."

I guessed with them that her parents would not approve. It was not a situation that you could swallow like mineral oil. The spawning habits of today's young are difficult, even when they terminate in the Bible. The times are enough to make even the most liberated of mothers wish for the old days of congenital, female distaste for sex. Even young mothers wonder if their own bleeding heart will someday be on the altar of the sex god. Bill was wonderful in his way, but Pixie probably would never live a life that her mother could understand. Pixie had run away, but her mother probably couldn't comprehend the depth of the running away. To Mother, it was probably a surface runaway. She was apt to reason that Pixie had gotten with the wrong friends, or hadn't wanted to go back to school because her grades were bad, or maybe she blamed herself. So many guesses and mostly wrong. But I knew that if Pixie were the true new breed, she didn't want to grow artificial tulips in a plastic pot like Mother and Daddy; she wanted no hypocrisy, no false values. She didn't like their standards, but still she didn't have too many of her own either. She got lost and ran away. The decision had nothing to do with love. She obviously loved her family, but she was confused and unhappy. The life that maybe satisfied Mother and Daddy couldn't satisfy her. She had been willing to sacrifice the comfort and love of home to search; it was THAT important. But maybe she hadn't known where or how to search. Drugs were handier, and she escaped that way.

Bill was not going to be her mother's dream son-in-law. He wasn't Lord Hathaway, and he probably wouldn't provide much of a castle for crystal and the family tea service. He was a good boy nevertheless, and Pixie had done well. I hoped her parents would see this, but I doubted it.

And Bill's parents. What of them? How would they like Pixie? They would take a shocked view of Pixie being pregnant. The grandbaby that really wasn't theirs? This is good?

Attitudes and Love

It crossed my mind to suggest that the baby could be adopted, but the fact of the little hitchhiker in their relationship didn't seem to bother them. So I filed this practical suggestion for another time. Everybody is too busy trying to make everybody else happy by their own personal standards. But Pixie and Bill didn't know how it was with babies. Or was it I that didn't know? Attitudes and love are what really make the difference. So they didn't have a job, a house, or even a crib, but they were sincere, not lazy. Perhaps it would work out.

"What will you do about the baby? Financially, I mean." I couldn't help wondering aloud.

"We'll stay on at the Psalm House until I know what to do," Bill answered. "We'll pray, and He'll show me. Right now I'm working on a Bible that will red-letter the symbolic blood thread of Christ."

He had lost me, but it didn't sound like a best-seller.

"You know how the Lord killed an animal to clothe Adam and Eve, and He demanded animal sacrifice all through the Old Testament—like the story about Cain and Abel. It's all in the Tabernacle story, too. It's lots of places, all the way to the blood of Christ to save us. The whole thing points the Way; you know what I mean. It's a real big story."

"I see," I said not seeing a thing but thinking Bible scholars had surely done this.

"The Bible needs to be specialized for study just like everything else is today," he stated, drifting off into the Jesus world. "I'd like to do one red-lettering all the prophecies about the First and Second Comings of Christ, too."

"Many scholars have worked it out," I couldn't resist saying.

"Oh sure, I know, but the Holy Spirit will guide me just as He has them."

Perhaps these special Bibles are just what the world needs. Who was I to question? I did not.

I let them out at the Psalm House to their tune of "God bless you. We'll pray for you." They had just about broken off my ears bilaterally, and my brain was numb. They were very young and vulnerable, but glowing and happy. Why was it too difficult to think that the Lord would take the unlovely, drug-infested youth to help the world? Medicine, church, and family love hadn't accomplished much. Maybe the new Thomases and Peters were at it again. The new breed of Christians weren't fishermen; in fact, they had seemed more than a little aimless until the Lord zapped them. All that these youths that had joined the various Jesus movements had in common with each other was desperation. Maybe when the truth couldn't come through the church, it found another stable. There was nothing new about that.

But some of my Jesus friends seem to lay down too

many "thou shalt not's." For instance, when praying and fasting suddenly came, everybody *had* to be at the Psalm House, and they didn't show for office appointments. Or was this my legalism? My private set of do's and don't's that had nothing to do with the Lord. I thought they lacked a sense of responsibility, but maybe they just felt more responsibility to the Lord than to my appointment book. They could be right. Still, when you lay down rules, you don't have to think, read, or study too much, you just 1-2-3 march. Yet that is not how it was with Pixie and Bill and most of the other Jesus group that I had seen. They were like a fresh breeze, expecting miracles and doing all those things that were for "those days," like speaking in tongues, healing and prophesying. "It is scriptural, you know," Pixie had said. And added teasingly, "Doctors get the pay, but the Lord does the healing."

The Jesus people whittled abortion down to nothing, and they didn't sleep around either. Perhaps the new breed would grow and multiply; some folks in our tract-filled land would find a renewed tract. A spirit of evangelism that is stirring in most churches gains impetus and fire from these Jesus friends. We don't give the bright-eyed young much credit, but that's where the credit belongs. There—and with the ministers and middle-aged who feel excited, not threatened.

CHAPTER THIRTEEN

Ethics

Emma Clements was definitely a student. She wore large glasses and a neat but plain dress. Her self-assurance helped to confirm her status even before I saw her books; the largest was *Behavioral Psychology*. She asked for an abortion and sounded as though she were cancelling a book order. She and her boyfriend, Howard, had been living together for two years.

"We both have eighteen months' study before we get our degrees. I know I'm early pregnant. I forgot a pill. So stupid of me." She paused and then asked, "How is the most professional and least expensive way that I can get this abortion?"

"Have you thought of any options to having an abortion?" I began.

"Doctor, Howard and I have talked this through.

There isn't any decision to be made between us, except how to expedite the matter!"

I referred her to a local clinic where I knew she would be aborted.

A Matter of Honesty

Emma was refreshing. There were no signs of hypocrisy here, no shadows from a steeple-surrounded culture. She was as bold an expression of pure ethics as Pixie was a bold expression of Faith. Honesty was the theme of both, and they stood squarely on their separate beliefs, poised for action.

Since abortion was the logical answer for this girl, we are back to the Supreme Court's decision, based on freedom of choice as constitutionally intended. As this country becomes less Godly, the inalienable rights of people must be separated from religion. The founding fathers separated church and state to strengthen religious faith. This was their way of preserving faith differences. Our problem today is different. We must give air space for freethinking, apart from religion. In 1948, the Supreme Court decided that religion could not be taught in public school buildings because such a practice violated the provision of the Constitution for complete church-state separation. The majority of the Court believed that the first amendment "rests upon the premise that both religion and church governments can best work to achieve their lofty aims if each is left free from the other within its respective sphere." In 1962-63, it was also decided that prepared prayers and devotional Bible reading in public schools was unconstitutional.

The public's furor over these issues suggests that people are concerned for the religious training of their children. Have churches failed? Have church-going parents failed? Should the public schools fill the religious vacuum? The Constitution was written with the dream of freedom. Freedom of worship at that time was protection for all faiths; one denomination could not force its beliefs on another. The reasoning is as true today as it was then, only the issues are different. It is now a question of religious morality against ethical morality instead of one brand of religion as opposed to another.

All the way from *The Scarlet Letter* to legalized abortions is a long, long way. It brings us to morality, and morality is the cause of much discussion today because change is affecting, fragmenting, and challenging our traditionally accepted way of life. If we are drowning in the questions of whether to abort or not to abort, to sex or not to sex, marry or not to marry, these are, at best, the substance of great topics. It is tragic that the young should be the ones most often to wrestle with such problems. However, they are certainly not only young problems but adult as well, whether within the personal context of action or in parental judgment. One of the saddest warnings of a lack of guidelines has been the youthful suicides in the twelve-to fifteen-year-old age group, usually by an overdose of parents' tranquilizers or sleeping pills. In the college group, it has been guessed that at least 100,000 college students will threaten suicide, almost 10,000 will make the effort; and one thousand or more will succeed. Such a situation holds so much heartbreak that adults cannot act as spectators; there is work to be done. There are values to be asserted in black and white.

Our children are a long way from Sesame Street and the good guys and bad guys of the western and police episodes. They are all the way to sex out of marriage and abortion. We parents are often so conditioned by soap operas, movies, books, and myriads of other influences, that we do not realize that we should be more than spectators.

Restless Adults

Adults, like adolescents, move restlessly from peer group to family and back again in different gradations. We are in a moral crisis and know it, but we don't seem to know what to do about it. The individual cannot change the tide, but he can control his own behavior. If he is a parent, he can influence his children and give them something solid. Concerned parents can do much if they will come out from behind self-erected fences. This is a duty and a most important function of the family unit; since morality is democratic, it is necessary to set an example. Few of us hide anything; we just like to think we do. Everyone stars somewhere in the sin battle.

This country seems to be moving toward ethical morality instead of religious morality. People have always felt that there were basic right and wrong ways, and that ethics establish this standard of right and wrong. The Ten Commandments and the Golden Rule, as principles, set up Western civilization's concept of ethics. Of the people sitting in churches today, it would be interesting to know how many are God-oriented and how many are ethic-oriented. Christians say there is only one poll that can show this conclusively, and that is the Lord's. Giving money and physical efforts to the church is certainly not committing our lives. We must look deeper into the heart to discern commitment. It is not that we are conscious hypocrites, but we are living on ethical standards of good behavior alone, and do not realize it. We don't need holy righteousness; the attitude that everyone is entitled to an opinion "as long as it is *mine*," does not help anything or anyone. We may not need to be hyperthyroid Christians like Pixie in the "Jesus People" chapter, but maybe something less extreme might spell it out just as well.

Many persons, young and old, stand torn by a suspected loss of religion, but they have not as yet stepped mentally into actual denial of faith and into freestanding ethics. No one can get into more trouble than such persons. They often vote for pleasure or the expediency of the moment, for excitement at the expense of society. This is neither religious *nor* ethical. Sex involving X number of partners and other problems such as alcoholism and drug abuse are typical expressions of both religious and ethical decay. The battle seems to involve everything except cannibalism—but Satan worship is on the move, and who knows? Maybe it's next.

The Shock of Discovered Evil

Meanwhile, "Satanism" is something from Hollywood until a friend's beloved Persian cat comes home with both eyes blinded, and the veterinarian says: "Now isn't this interesting? We've had several blinded cats lately. I just can't figure out what instruments were used. Somebody knew what he was doing, and he must sure hate cats!"

You don't know quite how to catalogue this bit of information.

Then your married daughter looks at a nice house in suburbia, and the recreation room is painted black. The real estate agent, says: "We are sorry about this room. It will take a little imagination to see what a great room it really is. The painters are coming tomorrow. We think a soft yellow will make it look big and airy again."

And then she adds, wonderingly: "Why would anybody paint the window panes black? And those dreadful black shades! There is no accounting for the taste of people these days!"

The agent notices the dripping white candles on the window sills; they have made a puddle of wax everywhere. "It's one thing to have bad taste, but it's quite another to be a bad housekeeper," she says, primly. And you think, "Could this have been a meeting place for Satan worshippers?" You've heard there were groups all over the city. People like sensational news. It's absurd, of course. Ridiculous! Or, is it?

And the next day a patient whose husband is a policeman happens to mention that last night he was sent to investigate a deserted church that was for sale. He had stumbled on the body of a derelict in the yard. Not too unusual, except that the body had broken bones and must have been dropped from the second story window. Another strange thing, the body appeared to have been drained of most of its blood. And the patient says, "Isn't that wild? They think it's Satan worship!"

The Infiltration of the Occult

You go to one of the local game shops to look for something new and fun for your sixteen-year-old son's birthday present. It's been hard to think of something different and inexpensive to add to the new water skis and wet suit. It's nice to have a little collection of presents on birthdays. You had a Ouija ™ board in mind but the clerk says, "You know, we just can't keep in those things. Everybody's buying them like crazy." And then she picks up a little box and says, "Tarot cards are something they all seem to like. We have an interesting new shipment." And you buy because you've heard that they are the in-thing. It's just as well about the Ouija ™ board, because you had a patient who went berserk over that fad, but she had been emotionally upset anyway. You had advised a psychiatrist, but her husband had shouted things about "head shrinkers" and vetoed the idea fast. Too bad. Because she's now institutionalized. You go home, and you hear a bizarre television newscast about Satan worshippers, and you are reminded of one of those sensational magazine articles you read on the same subject. The news media will certainly go to any length to dig up a story.

Thank goodness you don't have to worry about your own child! The birthday boy is safely at the movies with his girlfriend, and your fifteen-year-old has filched his Tarot cards. She's happily upstairs with a friend. They are giggling and having a great time with the cards. Your son had been interested, too. After the show, he and his date would probably give them a whirl. Those cards are a big success and not costly either. But you wonder what movie they are seeing. And what was that you read about the devil and the Tarot cards? Strange and unreal, isn't it?

The Satan thing is frightening. The world may need the old two thousand mile check-up. It's been about two thousand years since Christ, and since the great Greek Golden Age with its Plato, Aristotle, Stoics, and Epicureans.

Perhaps Satanism is just another example of a need for well-defined morals. And where do you begin? You begin with people like Pixie and Emma—the ones who really know where they are.

I feel that there should be a sharp dividing line between religious morals and ethical morals. One should not be half-ethical or half-religious. Such hypocrisy, conscious or unconscious, needs the light of day.

Every person should decide whether he chooses principles of behavior for the good of society or for the praise of the Lord. Faith calls this a decision for or against personal salvation. Ethics calls it a standard for personal living in civilized society.

Let's look at ethical morals. It seems to be trick or treat time everywhere. God's law excludes free love, adultery, and on into a list that includes killing, lying, stealing, and lusting. Ethics, for the preservation of society, has to put a jaundiced eye on killing and stealing, but in other cases it will not be so restricted. The new ethical sex morality claims it is not promiscuous. Sex is not used as entertainment, but as a personal commitment of love, though not related to family or marriage. It is not a happening as opposed to a relationship. Abortion, whether in married or unmarried state, has many feasible ramifications, and offers assurance of sex pleasure without procreation. Birth control brushes by the firing line, too.

As for religious morals, when was the last time you consulted with your minister? He will be able to make the distinction clear between ethics and faith.

The Point of this Chapter

In my medical dealings with Karen, the confused girl, Pixie, the fundamentalist girl, and Emma the godless, ethical girl, I saw an interesting fact. Karen of the I-don't-know rank said, "Is abortion murder? What do you think, Doctor?" Pixie of the Jesus faith said, "I'll pray and trust God to solve my problems like He promised." Emma of the intellectual cult said, "I know what to do." For the latter two women, there was no panic of decision. As I have repeatedly said, the abortion decision is for each individual to solve in the judgment of her belief. This is the crux of the abortion law and the spirit of freedom for women.

The Way It Worked Out

Of these three girls mentioned, Pixie had her baby. She got along fine in every way but her family's way. They didn't understand. The Lord kept giving Bill money, and he's going to a fundamentalist seminary now. I guess that he's still working on those Bibles. The other girls had their abortions, so I don't know what happened in their lives.

So what? I am not a theologian, but I am a practical doctor and need a good personal mental file with some degree of medical wisdom to handle my patients. The pregnant patient's body and mind must work together in the cause of health. I must play a part in the moral war, because as an obstetrician and gynecologist, I am reluctantly drafted. It is my belief that principles of morality need to be stressed in every phase of education in the same manner as sex and family-related problems. There is no way to have a civilization without rules of behavior. And isn't civilization what education is all about?

We can surely march to our own drums, but we must identify our cause. Morals are not plastic; they are alive and breathing. This moral war that our young have inherited is a devious one in which few advocates are either hot or cold. We need more updated health clinics to handle the medical problems of abortions as well as the other sex-related problems of gonorrhea and syphilis. Perhaps we also need soul-clinics to handle our conscience problems. Conscience is that thing that hangs around after yesterday's actions. I can't really defend this, but it sounds like a doctor-oriented response to a theological problem.

Our "Trojan Horse," legal abortion, may bring new thought to both ethics and religion.

Part Four: A Solution

CHAPTER FOURTEEN

Options to Abortion

The telephone rang one night about eight o'clock, and an anxious male voice said, "This is David McNabb. My wife Olivia used to come to you. Don't know whether you remember her or not—it's been several years. We moved out of town two years ago. I'm calling about my nineteen-year-old daughter."

When you've been in the medicine business a while, you develop a sixth sense that punches the button on "listen."

"About my daughter," he hurried, "could you do an abortion on her tomorrow?"

It was a raw question and put abortion in the same class as irrigating sinuses.

"Bring her to the office tomorrow, and let's talk it over," I stalled.

"Will you do the abortion?" he pressed.

"We'll talk it over," I repeated, and Mr. McNabb hung up.

When the Baby Is Unwanted

"You have to walk in my shoes to see what it's really like" is an old song with a worn track. The daily experience of dealing with many unmarried pregnant patients who do not want babies has given the obstetrician some insight into the size of those shoes. The options to abortion offer mental and multiple choices, if not physical ones.

Marriage

Since most abortions in my experience are at the request of the unmarrieds, marriage to the male who is the father to the baby seems the best solution, if conditions are favorable. The word "favorable" segments into considerations as to desires, how long the couple have been going together, age (maturity rather than years in question here), and the type of home that can be projected by the couple in conjunction with the parents on BOTH sides, if necessary. It should be remembered that children NEVER (seldom?) marry the type of boy or girl that their families think is right for them. No one can solve the question of marriage for the couple. This does not have to be hastily decided, but should be settled before the pregnant one gets "the normally nagging, cranky personality" so often seen in maternity and never understood by loud, rather uninformed males regardless of age.

In the past, almost every obstetrician has put "jump the gun babies" in premature nurseries. I have placed infants there who weighed eight pounds and were so oversized for the bassinet that they needed kneepads to avoid abrasions. "Social prematures," we called them. Any patient could leave her baby in the hospital for twenty-four hours or longer after she went home in order to seal the impression of the early birth. Two weeks later, the pediatrician would receive accolades for the wonderful care he instigated to cause the rapid weight gain. In the world of hypocrisy, the deception seemed to warrant the social results. Today's more honest young peer group does not see any stigmata in the obvious fact that the wedding date is less than nine months from the delivery.

The long-range option, as opposed to a quick and easy decision of abortion, is often more practical for the future emotional and mental health of all concerned. My thinking is mostly directed to the problems of unmarried pregnancy, but unwanted married pregnancy is similar. If there already is a mistake in the marriage department, the serious questions here often become ones of convenience, finances, home atmosphere, or divorce. There are many tragedies of genetic origin, too. Detached advice from a doctor, minister, or marriage counselor will help.

There are options to abortions for unwed pregnancies: (1) Marriage; (2) Continuance with baby though single.

Adoption

We have come a long way since the basket for unwanted babies was placed outside the foundling home.
Found-ling—what a sad root the word has. By definition,
a foundling is a child found after it has been abandoned
by its parents. You don't see the same thing in nature.
Birds and bees follow a prescribed course; it is human
parents (with the gift of a brain that reasons!) who
abandon their helpless young.

After World War I, the United States became a model
for adoption methods and now surpasses all other countries in humane placement of unwanted children. The
"reliable gossip" of battle lines between "good genes
are everything" and "environment is the key" have declared a truce because adopted children with bad genes
have succeeded, and adopted children with good genes
and bad environment have likewise succeeded. Or, vice
versa the whole thing. Anyway the truce has given breathing privileges to unwanted babies. Currently the demand
for adopted babies far exceeds the supply. Pregnancy
rates are rapidly increasing, while birth rates are drop-
ping. The desire of unmarried mothers to keep babies
accounts for the dramatic drop in available adoptees.

Good homes can be found quickly for babies, and
this is usually settled before birth. Social workers carefully screen families in their placement of children. They
counsel separately with the natural and expected parents,
co-ordinating the requirements and interests of both.
The normal needs of the babies are the first considera-

tions. A careful examination of the adoptive family combines counseling, study, and home visits. The record is filed. Usually the waiting time for the adoptee is very long. Statistics seem to indicate that one in four applicants are accepted. Those rejected either do not meet the qualifications, or there are no babies available.

The above is explained in order to assure the mother who gives her baby for adoption that her baby will probably receive more love and a healthier environment than she may be able to give. In twenty years of practice, I have never had a patient regret this legal means of adoption, and I have had many return to me for planned babies. One point that may be stressed here is that the mother should be told the sex, size, and whether or not any abnormalities were present. The mother is relieved by the fact that she had a normal baby and that she has helped another family's need; but, above all, she is assured that her child will have an excellent home. This reaction may not be immediate but settles comfortably into her mind and emotions within a few weeks after delivery and remains throughout her life. The guilt of having destroyed a life is never present, and a few months out of her life have not made the difference that she thought.

If the pregnant patient desires to keep her condition a secret, there are many homes in cities other than where she lives that are available for complete care and adoption procedures. A qualified home will be recognized as such by either the state or federal government and will definitely have the mother's, as well as the baby's, interests at heart.

An obstetrician often sees on the same day: (1) a pregnant woman who does not want her baby; (2) a totally sterile couple with little or no hope for an available adoption.

Since we can no longer encourage the sterile couple by the promise that they may obtain a foster child easily or without a long waiting period, we are seeing many otherwise happy marriages suffering from a seemingly hopeless problem. Most authorities advise against the private handling of adoption by the combining of doctor-minister-sterile couple-lawyer. The obstetrician has neither the time nor knowledge to research the background of either the natural parents or the proposed foster home. Lawyers and ministers are equally unqualified. It should be required by law, as in Connecticut and Delaware, that a child be placed by a recognized social agency. An exception may be made when a mother surrenders her child to relatives, but even this suggests many potential hazards. Inbuilt pyschological problems here are easy to see and quite often lead to a train of emotional conflicts, not the least of which is the natural mother's desire in later years for child custody. The social worker within an established agency is the best channel for the welfare of all concerned.

Keeping the Baby, or, Single Parent Keeps Baby

The eighteen-year-old-plus group often keeps the baby. At times, sixteen-year-olds do so (with total approval of their peers), but the parents of the pregnant girl ALWAYS take a grim view of such a solution until the baby is born; THEN THEY ACT AS IF IT WERE THEIR IDEA TO HAVE THIS CHILD. This is especially true with the younger grandparents, thirty-five to forty-two—plus or minus a few years either way.

Recently, a fifteen-year-old patient came to my office with her mother. The complaint was an irritating vaginal discharge. No history of pregnancy was obtained. Examination showed that the girl was about six months pregnant. Being tall and thin, she was able to hide her condition from her parents. The mother was horrified, and a large crying scene ensued. There are days when the obstetrician's office is up to its windowsills with tears. These two cried so hard that they left the office without another coherent word. The day was a failure for me, but three-and-a-half weeks later I received a phone call from the fifteen-year-old's mother. Her daughter was having terrible stomach pains; I diagnosed labor contractions and sent her to the hospital. On admission, she was found to be in labor and later gave birth to a premature infant weighing four pounds and three ounces. Six weeks later, infant, mother, and new grandmother were all in the office beaming with proud maternalism. Quite a contrast to the first reaction of total rejection! Everyone loves the miracle of a baby; "Baby Power" is the same tremendous power that even primitive man could not resist. It will be wonderful when "every baby is a wanted baby" (as the bumper stickers read), but, in the meantime, don't underestimate the power of babies and a mother's love.

Subsequent love and care require the parents' patience and discipline. Certainly this should be every baby's birthright. They do not behave like dolls, and if the woman is not prepared for sacrifice, she should not consider the possibility of keeping the baby.

Conclusion

In the confusion and desperation of unexpected pregnancy, many women cannot think of options to abortion. They don't realize it, but their bodies have some major physical changes which affect their emotions, causing faulty judgment. The hormonal imbalance present in early pregnancy causes lack of insight. The mother-to-be is depressed and irritable. Nausea is frequent. These complaints are seen even in a planned and happy pregnancy. Add them to the social conflict of an unmarried pregnancy, and we have a person with poor insight and resulting bad judgment.

With the young, the family and peer group are equally important.

Family

The mother is often the backbone of the family. Father is usually no help in this situation. His pregnant, unmarried "little girl" causes him confusion, hurt, frustration—and anger. Mother, alone, or with the minister or doctor, can break the news to Father. She can also discuss the options with him from a *female* point—which is very important. Many pregnant young are totally surprised by the lack of a very vocal reaction when they confront their mothers with this problem. She, however, must be reminded that no hasty decision is necessary, and family love is greater than mistakes. Sensible "mother-type" reactions are on the levels of maturity and wisdom, because hysteria doesn't help either as an attitude or an example.

Peer Group

If the female with the unwanted pregnancy has friends who freely discuss their sexual exploits, the abortion is usually a topic of conversation. If a secondary or even primary contact of the possible abortee has had a pregnancy interruption and makes no secret about it, the pregnant one often follows the same route. She does not think of options to abortion or the possibility of delayed adverse reactions.

If the peer group is rather secretive about pregnancy interruption, the distressed female often seeks advice from Planned Parenthood, Birthright, or some like agency. If she goes to a medical abortion mill and she is advised that she is pregnant and that they will do the abortion for a specified sum, giving no options, I strongly advise her to contact one of the above agencies. *A hasty decision is unnecessary.* The family doctor or minister often can give aid and advice, too. Regardless of the source of advice, the woman must decide for herself. She has time to consider options. Two weeks doesn't make that much difference in early pregnancy.

Act maturely in solving this very emotional problem. Get all sides of the question. Think these over, and then act. My words are easily written, but the problem you have is great. The searching for opinions can prevent possible emotional trouble in years to come.

Part Five: Medical

CHAPTER FIFTEEN

First Intercourse

"I can't believe I'm pregnant," Louise said. "It all seems like a nightmare. I didn't enjoy it that much, the sex I mean. I was mostly scared."

Louise was a beautiful eighteen-year-old blonde who was planning an abortion. "Why didn't I enjoy it? Is something wrong with me?"

"No," I said. "You're normal."

She looked at me in disbelief, "You surely can't mean it!"

Yes, I did mean it. That's often how it is with first intercourse. There's many a bride that will say "Amen" to that one.

As an obstetrician and gynecologist, my main concern regarding the first intercourse of a female is directed to physical factors. The mental factors are also observed by those in my specialty, but, because we are not sexologists, psychiatrists, or psychologists, we cannot offer expert theories concerning motivations of this first act. However, since there seems to be an over-celebration of sexual freedom, we need to give honorable mention to the power of the peer group again.

Pessimistically thinking, it would seem that youths live in a bewildering world of choices involving pills, sex, or marijuana—plus. This is certainly not inevitably true for the intelligent youth, but the set of choices is easily available as temptations. In regard to sex, the peer group has a terrific overlay—no pun intended. The "follow the group" motive is present as well as just plain curiosity. We know the physical trauma involved in first intercourse, but we don't know the woman's mental response. Of course, there is usually a feeling of guilt; but after all, group acceptance means joining the pack and going "tourist class."

In the majority of cases, first intercourse hurts. The female may have a clitoral orgasm because there is no pain to that, but the vaginal penetration of the male organ into the unused vagina can be very traumatic, with pain being the most important element experienced. The messiness of the male sperm spilling on her perineum often turns her off. These repulsions are often subjugated because she doesn't want to appear "abnormal" to her partner.

In the brides-to-be who are seen for premarital examinations and instructions, there are specific physical problems presented which must be overcome. The spastic or too-tight vagina, caused physically or by the contraction of the vagina due to fear, inexperience, and other factors, is painful. A timeworn anecdote has two salty sailors describing their honeymoon. One brags about how many times he and his wife had intercourse on the bridal night. The other replies that he had had intercourse only once because his wife "wasn't used to it." It's a crude story, but it accurately describes 99% of all females' first experience.

"Honeymoon Cystitis"

There is also an aftereffect that causes pain within a day or so. The bladder of the female may be traumatized. She has "honeymoon cystitis," which manifests itself with burning on urination and with having to void every few minutes. There is urgency about this—when you have to go, you have to go. This condition is painful.

There is always the probability of contracting a venereal disease. Recall the warnings on television? Some young, pretty girl is walking on a beach or near a stream. The warning states, "She doesn't know she has gonorrhea." The fact is that V.D. in the female, in the first stages, or in early development, is often without symptoms. All doctors wish it would show an early, painful syndrome, but it doesn't. So there is another worry after first intercourse. Only a doctor or special health clinic can diagnose these cases of syphilis and gonorrhea which obviously must receive early therapy to prevent advanced complications to the body. One of the most frequently seen complications is the inability to have babies due to the fact that the gonorrhea caused scars to block the Fallopian tubes.

Every girl should give the boyfriend the Fickle-Fred test. Mate selection is important. Does he really love you? Is he just making another sex hit? It's well-established that the sex act doesn't create or generate love. It's a physiological, emotional communication which may or may not stem from love. If the boyfriend's attitude changes from tenderness to "It's late, and we'd better get home" after he's satisfied—watch out. His love is more shallow than you supposed. If he sometimes seems to avoid you, let him go. It isn't love. He will fade away sooner or later, and sooner is better.

There are many physical traps and man-traps on the girl road. It's easier to march to your own drumbeat by moonlight than sunlight. Cystitis, painful intercourse, fear of venereal diseases, and possible pregnancy are lonely problems even with the most sympathetic of boyfriends. Practically speaking, there is not too much "free" for the young girl in love.

CHAPTER SIXTEEN

Doctors' Attitudes

"I wish doctors would agree on abortions," Ms. Stallings said and frowned. "I just don't know what to do."

She was twenty-six years old, soon to be married—and pregnant. She lived according to certain "contemporary" personal standards. The diaphragm had failed as birth control. She had been to a doctor friend of mine for advice. He had talked with her gently and wisely, but his opinion was different from mine.

Ms. Stallings had seen one too many doctors. Abortion was not our decision; it was hers. Doctors can't always agree; we look through the eyes of our personal experience. Some of us have blue eyes and others brown eyes.

Through the ages, women have been left with the end product of either a planned or unplanned pregnancy. For a like period of time, some females have been trying to "do away" with their pregnancy. They have run the gamut from herbs prescribed by the old witch to the modern day abortion clinics.

Just as legal abortions have updated women, so have doctors who enlisted in the cause performed abortions in a manner that required police authorities to intervene. They wanted test cases to force the courts to change the rule. Some of these doctors were very dedicated, putting their reputation as well as their practice on the battle line. As we have said, both the abject poverty seen in the ghetto areas as well as the population explosion were motivating factors.

There are many reasons for the hesitancy of those in the medical profession to perform abortions. Just as some campaigned for abortion, others did not. All doctors have been trained to save lives, not to destroy them. In abortion, it is the doctor who kills, not the patient. It is on his private score pad and personal conscience. But, each abortion case is different; and varying medical opinions are also present.

What is it in one doctor's experience that makes him weigh the responsibility of a decision so much longer than another? Most "seasoned" doctors in private practice are more reluctant to accept wholesale abortions than the younger ones who are conditioned by institutionalized medicine. It is often the young doctor, resident or intern, who staffs the abortion clinics. He is very qualified to do the pregnancy interruption.

What is a doctor's training like?

The Typical Experience

In his freshman year in medical school, he works and studies hard, and he dissects a cadaver. The sophomore year involves more routine study. Pathology includes the observation of autopsies from the stand. Seeing a freshly-dead body cut open may cause fainting or vomiting. The "old cadaver" had become a close friend in anatomy class—but this is different. A third year student is turned loose on patients and is called "Doctor." Hard work has earned him this title. He is not to be called "Doc." He wants the status of the full six letter word and has earned it. He does histories and physicals and observes operations. The senior year, he is a little more polished—and hardened toward "cases." He sees illness as easily curable, arrested, or a noncurable case; if he correctly diagnoses a difficult medical problem, it is "ego-gas" in his tank. And then he becomes a doctor—with a diploma to prove it, and he goes to a hospital for further training and study, for diagnostic and operative procedures. He evaluates practicing doctors and forms opinions of his own. He works; he is tired; and he is always busy; but he learns. And then it is time for the responsibility of his own practice. It is at this point that patients become persons instead of cases, and his attitude changes fast.

In regard to abortions and obstetricians, several incidents may have changed the young doctor's values in the period between school and practice. He may have seen a beautiful young girl die from an abortion or one who had had a psychosis from a too hasty decision. In private practice, "routine" changes to "personal." The cold factors of education blend with attitudes of life, experience, and all those other wonderful factors that make him "human" in the full size of the word.

"Seasoned" doctors working and studying in institutions are still another breed. They advance medicine, and their strides are great. They tend to specialize in work that is good for the masses with less consideration for the individual. A "good case" is a complicated, serious one with medical complexities. They are apt to see many more patients daily than the city doctor because their business is with the crowds in the waiting rooms of a teaching hospital. Here, one doctor works big and small miracles with many each day.

All of this is to say that doctors' attitudes on abortion vary. They have rights of decisions, too. Some of the best debates on abortion happen spontaneously in the doctors' lounge at the hospitals. It will continue to happen because the "Trojan Horse" travels everywhere.

CONCLUSION

I covered in medical armor the validity of our deductions and summations with the knowledge they may not be acceptable to other branches of endeavor. Everyone must work from a broader base of education than that of his own narrow specialization.

This has been a "together-book." As the "doctor-in-the-house" [Patterson] has said, "it is often feminine writing. I apologize, but it is my [Janet's] nature." He criticized, praised, and guided me thought by thought in the abortion question, which is a big one in his daily experience. The one-of-us could not have done this book without the other. Here is male-female equality and a good marriage. There were fights and scrapes along the way, but, as in all solid togetherness, we worked out most of our differences as we traveled from page to page. It seems worth it, for now we have a book together. Isn't it often this way on the together-road?

The experiences and thoughts are true in his experience but are reported through a woman's eye; they have been sifted down to "Woman's" thinking and reasonings. I have relentlessly refused his "one-two-three," sensible approach, but I know it would have made my reasoning appear more logical and astute. My hyphenated words have bothered him, too, but then there are places that one word simply couldn't express my meaning.

I haven't been able to organize my thought processes in the first paragraph of each chapter or followed logical development to the neat conclusion that would please my publisher. But lots of women will understand. Men have a way of aging women in ways like this, but theirs is a losing battle. Women can't help but be women. Perhaps it has to do with those changing "seasons and cycles" the Lord (or nature) gave us.

P.S.:

In the spirit of the times, I hastily add that just as many men as women do not think in terms of 1-2-3 and do not organize their thoughts in the first paragraph. It is much better to admit that I am a disorganized person. I am completely satisfied with the trait, and not in the least concerned about "seasons and cycles." Who really cares? It's each to her (or his) own bag of tricks.

JANET PATTERSON